MRS. McTHING

MRS.

OXFORD

McTHING

A Play by

MARY CHASE

Illustrations by MADELEINE GEKIERE *and* HELEN SEWELL

UNIVERSITY PRESS   *New York*   1952

PRINTED IN THE UNITED STATES OF AMERICA

To

ROBERT WHITEHEAD

*because he loved it for so long
and produced it in the theater
with such care, this book of the
play* Mrs. McThing *is gratefully
dedicated by the author.*

As produced by ANTA

(Robert Whitehead, Managing Director)

with

HELEN HAYES

Jules Munshin

Brandon de Wilde

THE CHARACTERS

MRS. HOWARD V. LARUE III, a rich widow
CARRIE, a nursemaid
SYBIL, a parlormaid
MAUDE LOOMIS, a friend
GRACE LOOMIS, a friend
EVVA LOOMIS, a friend
NELSON, a bodyguard
BOY
ELLSWORTH, a chef
VIRGIL, a waiter
DIRTY JOE, a gangster
THE STINKER, a gangster
POISON EDDIE, the chief gangster
MRS. SCHELLENBACH, Eddie's mother
HOWAY, an only child
MIMI, a little girl
MRS. MC THING, a witch
BERT, a policeman
SECOND POLICEMAN

ACT I

Scene 1:   The morning room, Larue Towers.
          Late afternoon of a summer day.

Scene 2:   Shantyland Pool Hall Lunchroom.
          The same day, an hour later.

Scene 3:   The same—a few minutes later.

ACT II

Scene 1:   Shantyland Pool Hall Lunchroom.
          A few days later.

Scene 2:   The morning room, Larue Towers.
          That night.

ACT ONE

SCENE 1

THE TIME: *The present. A spring afternoon.*

THE SET: *The curtain rises slowly and we now look into a room rich and beautiful; velvet draperies of lavender, walls painted with figures of Grecian goddesses, gold chairs and tables, satin-covered sofas. An immense crystal chandelier hanging from the ceiling, glitters like a thousand diamonds.*

A white and gold staircase rises gracefully at one side of the stage and ends at a door painted with gold and silver.

There is a deep window on the right side of the stage which allows us to glimpse gardens and fountains outside.

There is another door at the left side of the stage below the staircase which leads into the music room where there is a golden harp and a golden piano inlaid with ivory.

But the most interesting object in this room is the full-length, life-size oil painting of a boy which hangs on the wall, stage center, above the satin-covered sofa.

This boy has blonde hair and mischievous blue eyes. He is wearing a blue velvet suit with white lace at the collar and cuffs and he looks as though this suit annoyed him very much. He looks as though he would like to jump out of the painting, and play cops and robbers, run, yell and jump over chairs. But he doesn't.

13

*He stands silently and proudly, like a young prince,
one hand on one hip as he looks out over this handsome room with the gold furniture, the satin and
crystals.*

*Is this a young prince? Is this the throne room of an
ancient palace?*

No. The boy is not a prince. He is HOWARD V.
LARUE IV *and the woman we now see who is standing
alone on the stage at the window looking out is not a
queen. She is the boy's mother,* MRS. HOWARD V. LARUE
III, *and this is the morning room of their home, Larue
Towers, in the very best section of town.* MRS. LARUE
*is holding in her hands, not a scepter, but the coach
of an electric train.*

*She is a pretty woman and she is wearing a long silk
dress of pale lavender and diamond earrings in her
ears.*

*We see in the distance a beautiful wall of Blue, Blue
Mountains, their peaks tipped with snow. They rise
high and sharp like giant waves of a great sea tossed
against a paler sky.*

MRS. LARUE *often stands at her window and looks
out at the Blue, Blue Mountains. She looks at them
across her green lawns and gardens and trees. They
are the only things she can see from her window
which she does not own. Perhaps this is why they
fascinate her so much.*

*But now she turns and looks away from them. Some
one is entering the room. It is* CARRIE, *the boy's nurse.*

CARRIE *is a plump, motherly-looking woman wearing a gray dress with white collar and cuffs. She is
carrying a small ivory tray on which sits a gold telephone with a long white cord, a plug at the end.*

15

CARRIE. Mrs. Larue—telephone. It's Dr. Hyslop, ma'am. He says you left a call for him. (CARRIE *now pushes the telephone plug into the wall and hands the telephone to* MRS. LARUE.)

MRS. LARUE. Dr. Hyslop, the dentist? I'll speak with him. But don't go, Carrie. I want you. (*She walks to the telephone; her silk dress rustles and the diamond earrings in her ears glisten like tiny crystal chandeliers.*)

Hello, Dr. Hyslop? This is Mrs. Howard V. Larue. I'm calling you about my son. (*She turns and looks at the portrait as though she were also saying: "My son whose oil painting hangs on the wall of this room."*) Doctor, would you be good enough to come here tomorrow to Larue Towers on Van Tyne Road and bring your dentist chair and look at his teeth. I'll take care of the expense. After school? Oh, Doctor, my son doesn't go to school. He has a tutor. What time shall you come? Let me think. He has lessons until noon— horseback riding until two—rest until—we'll postpone his horseback ride. Come at two. And Doctor, you must promise me something. You must promise me you will not hurt him, will you, Doctor? He is very sensitive. And Doctor, please bring your credentials with you. Otherwise, the guards might not let you in at the gate. Thank you, Doctor—until tomorrow. (*She hangs up the telephone.*) Carrie—!

CARRIE. Yes, ma'am.

MRS. LARUE (*looking at the toy train in her hand*). I was up in Howay's playroom this morning. Is this the only car left of his electric train?

CARRIE. Yes, ma'am—out of eighteen cars—the only one left.

16

MRS. LARUE (*again looks at the car. She sighs*). And the little engine—that dear little engine—is that gone too?

CARRIE. Oh, ma'am, the engine has been gone over a week now.

MRS. LARUE. I don't understand this. Who is stealing my son's toys? And how can he get onto the grounds?

CARRIE. Who knows that? But whoever it is, he'd have to be pretty nimble to climb those high walls and pretty quick to get past the watchman and the bodyguard.

MRS. LARUE. Carrie, you don't suppose it could be anyone in this house?

CARRIE. (*She is offended at this question.*) You mean me, ma'am? Or Sybil, the parlormaid? Or Nelson, the bodyguard? Or the ten gardeners? Or the cook? Or the assistant cook? What should any one of us want to be stealing parts of a boy's electric train? We are too big for such things.

MRS. LARUE. Oh dear—oh dear! If this keeps on Howay will have nothing left to play with, Carrie!

CARRIE. Oh, I wouldn't say that, ma'am. Nothing has happened to his little pony and cart; or his little movie theater off his bedroom where he sees his Western movies, or his swan motorboat on the lake or his——

MRS. LARUE. But he always loved this train especially. I'll have to call my lawyer in the morning and ask him what to do about this, and please tell Nelson to hire another watchman to patrol the grounds at night. Since only toys are missing, the thief must be a child.

CARRIE. (*A mysterious look crosses her face as though she knows a secret she would not tell.*) Perhaps, ma'am.

MRS. LARUE (*as she puts the train car down on one of the little gold tables*). I had this train made especially for Howay. See, Carrie, the little seats are upholstered in red leather. See the green carpeting on the floor—just like a real train. I wanted Howay to have the most perfect electric train ever built. I used to like to pretend I was a passenger, sitting on one of those little seats, riding away—far—far—off. Oh yes, my boy and I have had lots of fun playing with this train. Where is my son now?

CARRIE. (*She looks at her wrist watch.*) He finished studying his arithmetic and he's gone for a walk on the grounds with his bodyguard.

MRS. LARUE. (*She walks over and looks out of the window.*) Walking on the grounds! But that's just what I told him to do. How odd! Have you noticed lately that he does exactly what I tell him to do at exactly the time I tell him to do it?

CARRIE. (*And now her voice is strange and bitter and again that "I know a secret" look passes over her face.*) Oh yes, ma'am. I've noticed that all right.

MRS. LARUE. It's amazing the way he has changed in the last few weeks.

CARRIE. I loved him the way he was.

MRS. LARUE. (*Her voice is impatient.*) Oh, of course, Carrie, so did I. But you will have to admit he was sometimes pretty hard to handle.

CARRIE. He used to be a normal American boy.

MRS. LARUE. (*Now she is more impatient with* CARRIE.) Oh Carrie, why do you always sigh so and act so peculiar about Howay lately? You used to be devoted to him.

18

CARRIE. He is not the same boy.

MRS. LARUE. I don't understand you any more, Carrie. Of course he is the same boy.

> (*At this point we hear sounds outside the room. It sounds like a barnyard cackling with hens.*
>
> *Enter* SYBIL, *the parlormaid. She is a pretty young girl wearing a dark green uniform with a tiny white apron and a small ruffled cap on her head. She now stands very straight—just so. We know she is about to announce the visitors who have only just arrived in the hallway outside.*)

SYBIL. Miss Loomis, Miss Maude Loomis, Miss Grace Loomis!

LARUE. (*Her face breaks into a smile.*) The Loomis girls! Carrie, go find Howay and have him come in here. He might like to have tea with us.

> (*Enter the Loomis girls. They are three women, all smiling, all sputtering. The sounds they make sound like "Pishpash—pish—pash—cut a cut a cutt cut."*
>
> *They are wearing feathers and ribbons and laces, ruffles and pleats, godets and inserts. They carry lace handkerchiefs. They rush over to* MRS. LARUE *and kiss her. Now they sit down on the sofa.*
>
> *The youngest sister,* MAUDE, *looks eagerly at the golden dish full of chocolates on the little gold table. She would like to reach out and take several pieces. But she knows she must wait until they are passed. So now she sees the piece of lace pinned onto the back of a chair. It is lovely cream-colored old lace. It is so beautiful. She touches it. Her older sister sees her.*)

19

EVVA. (*The eldest sister. She wears blue.*) Maude!

MAUDE. (*The youngest sister. She wears pink. To* MRS. LARUE.) Belle, don't ever throw this lace away. If you tire of it, give it to me. It would make a wonderful dickey for my green suit. (*She unpins it from the chair and holds it up at her neck.*)

EVVA. (*Oh but she is ashamed of her! Doesn't she know how to act yet?*) Put it back, Maude. Belle wants it on that chair.

MRS. LARUE. I'll save it for you, Maude.

GRACE. (*The middle sister. She wears brown.*) It does look nice on her, Evva.

EVVA. Yes, it does. But she must keep her hands off it all the same.

MRS. LARUE. My dear friends, you haven't been out here to see me in over a month. I've missed you.

EVVA. We've been attending those lectures at the institute. (*She sees her sister still fooling with the lace on the chair.*) Put it back, Maude. Belle said she would give it to you before she threw it out.

GRACE. But sister, it does look better on Maude than it does on that chair.

EVVA. Sisters! (*She is very cross at both of them.*) Drop it—drop it!

MRS. LARUE. Girls, I have asked the cook to make us some of those little pecan cookies you like so well—for our tea.

EVVA. (*This makes her so happy.*) Belle, you are sweet—— (MAUDE *will not leave the lace alone.*) Put it back, Maude. Stop pulling at it. Fold your hands and sit quietly.

20

MRS. LARUE . . . and I thought I would ask Howay to have tea with us.

> (*As she says this a strange look crosses the faces of all three sisters. The eldest sister looks worried. The middle sister looks frightened. The youngest sister stops fooling with the lace and looks as though she would like to go home. Howay have tea with them? This is a dreadful thought. But they know they must not tell his mother they think he is a dreadful boy because then they might not get the pecan cookies. So EVVA frowns, gives her sisters one of those "be quiet—and let me talk" looks. Then she coughs, clears her throat and speaks in a very gentle and soft tone.*)

EVVA. Ask Howay to have tea with us? Belle, dear, do you think that's wise?

MRS. LARUE. Wise? Why not?

GRACE. (*She has been warned to keep quiet but she doesn't.*) The last time we were here he threw cookies at Evva.

MAUDE. (*She cannot keep still.*) And he kept running that little black rubber mouse all over the tablecloth. Grace got sick.

GRACE. And he kept squirting Maude with a water gun!

EVVA. (*She is cross with them! Why can't they keep quiet when they are told to keep quiet? Don't they know that if you tell a boy's mother he is naughty she will almost never give you pecan cookies?*) Girls—sisters! (*She smiles gently at* MRS. LARUE.) Howay is very sweet. Of course he did run that little mouse over the table and he did squirt Maude with a water gun but we must

21

not judge anybody. Perhaps he was not feeling well that day.

MAUDE. But remember that bad language he used when we tried to kiss him?

EVVA. Maude Loomis!

MAUDE. And he made a face at you. Remember?

> (*Here* MAUDE *sticks out her tongue and puts her thumbs in her ears and wiggles her fingers to show the face he made. She looks very silly. She really does not know how to make this face. She has not practiced it enough.*)

EVVA (*who would like to spank her*). I think I can remember, Maude, who made faces at me and who didn't.

> (*Now into the room comes* NELSON. *He is a bodyguard. He has two guns at his belt and a peaked cap.*)

NELSON (*takes off his cap*). How do—how do. I've brought him in, Mrs. Larue.

> (MRS LARUE *and the Loomis sisters all rise and look at the door at the top of the stairway.*
>
> *The door opens and they see a boy enter and walk slowly down the long stairway. This boy is wearing a gray suit with short pants, long black socks to his knees. He has a white collar with a black silk tie, tied in a bow. His hair is combed so smoothly and parted so perfectly that not one hair is out of place. He looks as though each morning he stood before the mirror and counted them. Fifty-nine million on the left side, thirty-two million and five on the right side. He is wear-*

*ing white gloves on his hands and a small black
beret cap on his head. Each button on his jacket
is buttoned. There is not a spot on his clothing
nor on his face.*

*As he walks down the stairs into his mother's morn-
ing room he does not walk too slowly in a loiter-
ing, hanging back fashion. Nor does he come too
quickly. He walks perfectly. When he is at the
bottom step he pulls a bell cord hanging from the
wall.*)

MRS. LARUE. Well, Howay—well, dear!

BOY (*removing gloves carefully, pulling each finger sepa-
rately so as not to rumple them but keep them smooth
for the next time he will wear them*). Very well,
Mother. I hope you are the same. (*He bows to her.*)

MRS. LARUE. Yes, dear.

(SYBIL, *the parlormaid, enters.*)

SYBIL. Did some one ring?

BOY. I did. Please take my hat.

(SYBIL *comes over and takes his hat.*)

SYBIL. Is that all?

BOY. Not yet. Take my gloves please. (*He places them
in her hand.*) Thank you.

(SYBIL *takes them out with her.*

*The boy now sees that his mother has guests. The
Loomis girls are looking at him with admiration.
He walks—not too slowly, not too fast—over to
them. He knows that one must be polite to one's
mother's friends. He smiles at them and bows.*)

How do you do, Miss Evva—how lovely you look.
(*He walks to the middle sister.*) Miss Grace, what a

23

pretty hat! (*He walks to the youngest sister.*) Miss Maude, you are younger every day. (*He waits.*) Well, aren't you going to kiss me?

> (*As he says this again we hear the sound of clucking hens as the Loomis girls rush forward and cover him with kisses. They hug him. They say things like "You darling!" "You adorable boy." "Kiss you?" "We could eat you up!"*

The boy looks very happy. He likes to be kissed by his mother's friends.)

MRS. LARUE. *(She looks at him wonderingly. Of course he is behaving as she had always hoped he would some day. But still—it seems so strange! She picks up*

the golden dish full of candy and passes it to her friends.) Girls, do help yourselves. These have cherry filling and nuts, too! (*The Loomis girls all help themselves. They take a bite and smile. Oh, how delicious! She passes the dish to the boy.*)

BOY. (*He frowns.*) Of course not, Mother. They would spoil my dinner. (*He now sees his mother take a candy.*) And what about your diet?

MRS. LARUE. (*She then remembers and sadly puts the candy back into the dish.*) Of course, dear. You're quite right. It is close to your dinner. It is nearly five o'clock. Why, it's about time for those radio programs —and the cops and robbers on television. Would you like to go to your room and turn it on for a while?

BOY. Oh, Mother, it is all such trash!

MRS. LARUE. Or would you like to have tea with the girls and me on the terrace?

BOY. Oh, Mother, may I please?

EVVA (*looking at this darling child*). Bless his heart. He wants to have tea with us.

GRACE (*also looking at him as if he were a piece of candy*). He is so dear. He has certainly changed.
  (MAUDE *is again fooling with the lace on the chair.*)

EVVA. Maude Loomis, will you keep your hands off that?

MRS. LARUE. She can't hurt it, Evva.

EVVA. I've told you, Maude, not to keep fingering other people's property.

MAUDE. I wasn't hurting it.

BOY (*with a sweet smile*). She just didn't stop to think, Miss Evva. She will do better next time, won't you, Miss Maude?

26

EVVA. I can't get over you, Howay. Just think—only a month ago you squirted us with a water gun.

BOY. I did! How could I have been so rude!

EVVA. Don't feel badly about it, dear. You were going through a phase. But you have come out of it.

MRS. LARUE. (*She is looking at the boy very closely.*) He certainly has—and so fast too!

EVVA. Which reminds me—speaking of bad boys—Mrs. McLucas is having a terrible time with that boy of hers. He's been breaking windows with a rubber beanie. It's costing her a fortune.

(MRS. LARUE *and the Loomis sisters all laugh.*)

BOY. Mother! You're laughing! It isn't funny, is it? Then why laugh?

MRS. LARUE. (*She stops laughing.*) No, I don't suppose it is, dear. But I remember, Howay, when you used to do things like that yourself. I was nearly frantic.

BOY. But aren't you happy that I have finally come to my senses, Mother?

MRS. LARUE. Of course, darling!

EVVA. Speaking of Mrs. McLucas—have you seen Mrs. Wilkins?

MRS. LARUE. I haven't see her—she called yesterday but I was out.

EVVA. I wonder how she looks?

BOY. I saw her. She has gained weight. (*The women look at him with much interest. He continues.*) She was wearing a brown tweed suit with a rump sprung skirt, green gloves with a beige hat. And Mother, there was a touch of egg yolk spilled on her blouse. Isn't she getting careless!

27

MRS. LARUE. (*She looks at him strangely.*) Imagine a boy your age noticing things like that?

BOY. (*He regards his fingernails. They are so pink and white.*) I knew you would wonder how Mrs. Wilkins looked, so I studied her carefully.

EVVA (*throwing him a kiss*). Now wasn't that thoughtful? Bless his heart.

> (CARRIE *comes in and announces that tea is served on the terrace.*)

MRS. LARUE. (*Her silk dress rustles as she rises.*) Thank you, Carrie. Girls. Howay, darling. Tea!

EVVA. (*She must speak to the boy. She goes to his side. She speaks in a low-pitched tone.*) Howay! Did Mrs. Wilkins let anything slip about dyeing her hair? I'm sure she does.

BOY. So am I. But she was very close mouthed about that. However, I will tell you what I gathered—— (*Here he looks at his hands.*) But first I must make myself a little more presentable before tea. Will you excuse me, please? (*He bows to the ladies and slowly, but not too slowly, walks up the long stairs to his own apartment. The women watch him, fascinated with him.*)

EVVA (*after he has gone through the door at the top of the stairs*). Belle Larue, that boy of yours is the most adorable little gentleman I have ever seen.

MRS. LARUE. (*There is just a slight frown on her forehead.*) Girls, you don't feel that he has suddenly become TOO grown-up, do you?

EVVA. How could anybody become TOO grown-up? My dear, he is perfect.

GRACE. You should be so grateful.

EVVA. Whatever method you used—write an article about it for the *Parents Magazine*. You owe it to them.

MRS. LARUE. (*She walks over and stands looking dreamily out of the window at those Blue, Blue Mountains.*) Girls, have any of you ever happened to hear of a person named Mrs. McThing?

(*The Loomis girls look puzzled at each other.*)

EVVA. Mrs. McThing—Mrs. McThing! Does she belong to the club?

GRACE. Have we ever met her socially, girls?

MAUDE. We'd remember if we did. If anyone said to me, "Miss Loomis, meet Mrs. McThing," I'm sure I'd have remembered it and looked carefully. Who is she?

MRS. LARUE. I don't really know. I think she must be new in the neighborhood. I understand she has a place up there in the Blue, Blue Mountains. (*She walks closer to the window.*) Look—can you see a place up there?

(*And now as we look again at the Blue, Blue Mountains, we can see that what seemed to be a snowy peak is really a white palace with domes and turrets—a tiny white palace it looks from here. But that is because the Blue, Blue Mountains are so far away.*

The Loomis girls walk to the window and look out.)

EVVA. There is no house up there—only snowy peaks. Does she live up there—this Mrs. McThing?

MRS. LARUE. I have never laid eyes on her; but about three weeks ago; one afternoon; just about this time of day——

EVVA. Yes—yes——

MRS. LARUE. Mrs. McThing's child—a ragged little girl;

29

climbed over the wall and I found her playing with
Howay down by the lake. I knew nothing about this
child. I had never met her parents. So, since I simply
cannot allow every child off the road who takes a notion
to come in these grounds and play with Howay——

EVVA. You never have allowed that.

MRS. LARUE. And what is the sense of my hiring a bodyguard for him and having a high wall around these
grounds if any ragged, dirty little girl off the road can
climb in here and play with him?

GRACE. You are positively right.

30

MAUDE. She might be full of germs—ugh!

MRS. LARUE. Do you know what this youngster had the audacity to say to me? She told me her mother was Mrs. McThing—a witch!

GRACE. A witch! Oh, don't children say the rudest things about their parents these days?

MRS. LARUE. And what's more, she told me that if I sent her home, her mother would do something to me.

GRACE. As if she could do anything to you, Belle!

EVVA. You didn't let her bluff you, I'll bet.

MRS. LARUE. I did not. I sent her home anyway. Oh, Howay was screaming and kicking—he wanted to play with her—but I was firm. And then I had a little talk with him about his responsibilities and what he owed me and this home of ours. He must have listened to what I said because the most amazing thing happened. The very next morning he was a different boy. He began to mind. His manners improved. And—well, you just saw him.

MAUDE. Oh, Belle, aren't you happy about the change in him?

MRS. LARUE. Oh girls! (*She looks again out at the Blue, Blue Mountains.*) Tell me. Is anybody really happy? Let us go have our tea.

(*They all go out the door leading to the terrace. But* MAUDE *darts back and runs quickly to the candy dish. She is putting a few pieces into the pocket of her flowered silk dress when her eldest sister,* EVVA, *who has turned, sees her and rushes back into the room.* EVVA *is very angry. But she keeps her voice low because she does not want* MRS.

31

LARUE *to know that she has a sister who will put candy into the pockets of a flowered silk dress.*)

EVVA (*shaking her slightly*). Maude Louise Loomis— put those back! (MAUDE *drops the candy back into the dish.*) That nine-year-old boy acts better than you do. If you can't keep your hands off things, I will never bring you any place again.

(*Sulkily* MAUDE *follows her sister off stage and onto the terrace. The stage is empty. A little breeze ruffles the velvet curtain. Then, from a door over at one side, there steals into the room a ragged little girl. Her eyes are brown and snappy. Her cheeks are pink. She wears a dress of brown calico, thick-ribbed black stockings and high-buttoned square-toed shoes. She sees the train on the little golden table. She runs quickly toward it, picks it up and runs back out of the room and disappears by the same door through which she came.*

CARRIE *comes in to straighten up the room as the* BOY *again comes down the staircase.*)

BOY. Carrie! Where is my geography book? I placed it in this room this morning.

CARRIE. (*There is a frown on her face; she cannot look at the boy.*) It doesn't seem to be here. Where did you have it?

BOY. I placed it on the table, where I always place it.

CARRIE. Sybil straightened up in here this morning. Maybe she knows.

(*The boy pulls the bell cord and* SYBIL *comes in.*)

BOY. If things were kept where they belong this would

not happen. Sybil, I had the *Rivers of North America* in here this morning.

SYBIL. You did! All of them? Congratulations!

CARRIE. He's lost his book, Sybil—his geography book.

SYBIL. Oh, book!

BOY. I placed it on this table. Will you please try to find it for me? Thank you. (*He leaves the room to join his mother and her friends at tea.*)

SYBIL (*when she is sure that he has gone*). Carrie, that kid! They didn't tell me nothing about him at the agency when they sent me out here to work. He gives me the creeps. Now if anybody else said they'd brought rivers in here, I'd know better, but when he said it I thought—well, maybe he would pull a trick like that. He's weird. That's what he is.

CARRIE. He's a stick, that's what he is.

(NELSON, *the bodyguard, comes back.*)

NELSON. Where's Mrs. Larue? The groom told me to tell her the boy's pony won't go near his oats again today. Every time the boy rides him, the pony won't eat.

CARRIE. (*A look of fierce joy crosses her face.*) The pony won't eat the day the boy rides him! The pony knows the secret. You can't fool a dumb animal!

NELSON. What do you mean? Where is Mrs. Larue?

SYBIL. Having tea with her friends and her son.

CARRIE. Her son! That isn't her son. Her son was stolen away that night; that creature having tea with her is a stick, I tell you, a stick——

NELSON. Who was stolen? What are you talking about? Are you trying to lose me my job. Nobody stole any boy.

33

SYBIL. Carrie, what are you saying—a stick?

CARRIE (*in a whisper*). Come here with me, both of you. (*She takes them to the windows.*) Look up there, see that little white palace where she lives.

SYBIL. Who lives? You're frightening me. Your voice is so scary.

CARRIE. Mrs. McThing—the witch. She got angry at Mrs. Larue the day she sent her little girl home. So that night she came here. She played her music and stole the real boy away. He followed that magic music down the road. Then she put in his place a stick—that looks just like him but ain't him. That boy on the terrace out there is the stick she left——

NELSON. Gee— Say, girls! Keep quiet about this, will you? Don't tell Mrs. Larue. She'd fire me. I didn't hear no music. I never saw Mrs. McThing——

SYBIL. Where did she take the boy—the real boy?

CARRIE (*sadly*). If I only knew——

NELSON. Not a word about this, understand—both of you. If his own mother doesn't know the difference, why start trouble. Forget about the pony—forget I said a thing.

SYBIL. Carrie—look—up there. There is a light in that little white house—see!

> (*The stage has darkened slightly and sure enough in the little white palace on the peak there are now lights burning, making it look like a toy house on cotton snow underneath a tree at Christmas time.* CARRIE *and* NELSON *and* SYBIL *draw together in wonder.*
>
> MRS. LARUE *comes into the room carrying an armful of red roses.*)

34

MRS. LARUE. Sybil, will you find some moist paper for these flowers and set them in the hall for the Loomis girls to take home with them?

SYBIL. Yes, ma'am. (*She goes out.*)

MRS. LARUE. Carrie—oh, Nelson—did you want something?

NELSON. Oh nothing. I just wanted to make sure the boy was okay.

MRS. LARUE. My son is with us, Nelson, having tea.

NELSON. Thank you, ma'am. (*He goes out.*)

MRS. LARUE. Oh, Carrie, it seems my friends assumed they might be invited to dinner, too. They told me their grandmother had told them they might stay if they were asked. So what could I do but ask them? Tell the cook to make some hollandaise and use the frozen raspberries.

CARRIE. There's plenty of everything in this house.

MRS. LARUE. Yes, but I hate these last minute things. I like to plan ahead. (*There is a ring at the telephone.* CARRIE *starts to pick it up, but* MRS. LARUE *reaches it first.*) I'll take this call, Carrie. You had better speak to the cook about the raspberries. (*She picks up the receiver.*) Hello! Howay? Howay? (CARRIE, *who has been on her way out of the room, now stops and listens, eagerly.*) Darling, what are you doing on the telephone? I just left you on the terrace this minute, with the Loomis girls. Are you on the garage telephone? Are you on the telephone in the boathouse? You're what? You're working in a pool hall? (*She laughs.*) Howay, stop that nonsense. I just left you on the terrace with the girls. You're down by the railroad tracks? Under the viaduct?

35

Howay, stop it. I've got a lot to do. The girls are staying to dinner and—lower Seventh Street—near the tracks? (*The boy has now come in from the terrace and he stands silently watching her. She does not see him.*) Howay Larue, you have never been in such a neighborhood in your life. What? You're not in the house at all? You've been gone for weeks? (*She now sees the boy standing in the doorway, looking at her. She looks at the telephone; a look of fear crosses her face. She jumps up quickly and drops the receiver into the cradle of the telephone as she stares at the boy.*)

CARRIE (*runs quickly to the telephone. She clicks the receiver*). Howay—Howay! (*She turns to* MRS. LARUE.) He's gone. I can't get him back. Where is he? You hung up on him. What did he say?

MRS. LARUE. (*She is still frightened. She is looking at the boy and then at the telephone.*) Carrie, Carrie, what has gotten into you?

CARRIE. (*She goes to her closer. Her voice is excited.*) Tell me, tell me, where did Howay say he was?

MRS. LARUE. Carrie, Carrie, calm down! That was not Howay on the telephone. Howay is there—see him. (*She points with a trembling finger at the boy who now looks at her.*) That was some strange child from some neighborhood down by the tracks—working, he said, someplace down there.

CARRIE. So that's what she did with him. She stole him away and she put him out to earn his bread among strangers. Oh, that creature——

BOY. Calm down, Carrie. Let me get you some water. (*He walks across the room.*) Or perhaps hot tea would be better. (*He goes out.*)

36

CARRIE. Let him get me nothing. Mrs. Larue, that stick is not your son. You mean to tell me you haven't felt the difference?

MRS. LARUE (*shocked*). Carrie! That boy is my son. He has been different, but boys grow up. They change and maybe we do feel sad about it. Do you think I like it? Don't you think I miss the fun he used to be? But time steals everything away from us, they say.

CARRIE. Time, is it? I wonder. Where did he say he was? Only tell me the street. I'll look for him. I'll find him.

MRS. LARUE. Look for whom—for what? For the past—for yesterday? You'll never find that. There is no such street. Stole him away—put something in his place! Look at him—can't you believe your eyes? (*She looks up at the portrait.*) He's exactly the same—except for the hair cut.

CARRIE. And can't you believe your ears? He told you it was Howay and you thought so, too. I know my boy. I've looked after him since he was born.

MRS. LARUE. And don't you think I know my boy? (*She is now becoming angry.*) Oh, I've had enough of this. Carrie, you need a rest. You'd better go visit your sister in Kansas City for a vacation.

CARRIE (*bitterly. She drops her head*). Thank you, ma'am.

MRS. LARUE. Oh, Carrie, you've suddenly made me feel horrible. Is that what you wanted?

(*The Loomis sisters now come into the room from the terrace. They look at the stern expression on* CARRIE's *face and the frightened expression on* MRS. LARUE's.)

EVVA. Belle, what's wrong?

MRS. LARUE. Evva—Maude—Grace—will you forgive me? I suddenly feel very upset. I feel—well—girls, would you mind if we had dinner together another evening?

EVVA. Of course not, dear. But what's wrong? Can we help?

MRS. LARUE. No, no thank you. (*She looks up and now sees the* BOY *who has come back and is standing in the doorway of the room.*) Oh, it makes me so angry. It's all such nonsense. Carrie is tired. We—she—oh, she's been putting some silly ideas into my head! It's such a fiendish thing to do, Carrie, really!

BOY (*goes over to her. His voice is disapproving*). Mother! Mother! Control yourself.

MRS. LARUE (*turning on him*). Control myself. I'd like to see you control yourself if some one told you what she just told me. If she were to tell you——

CARRIE. Tell me! Where did he say he was?

MRS. LARUE (*her voice rising*). Stop it! Stop it!

EVVA. The boy is right. Listen to him, both of you. Whatever it is, you can be grown-up about it. (*She turns to her sisters.*) And you, too!

MAUDE. I haven't opened my mouth. You can't be any more grown-up than that.

EVVA. I think we'd better go. We'll telephone you tomorrow, Belle. Come, girls.

MAUDE (*as she is leaving*). But Evva, grandmother told us we could stay to dinner and now Belle says we can't. Grandmother won't like that. She doesn't like people to go against her.

EVVA. Maude—shh-shhh—— (*They all go out.*)

38

BOY (*in shocked tone*). Mother! Aren't you going to the door with your friends?

> (MRS. LARUE *now turns and stares at him. She stares at him as though he were a ghost. He looks at her placidly, unashamed, as he sits very stiffly on the sofa. She moves over ever so slightly—away from him.*)

CARRIE. Mrs. Larue!

MRS. LARUE. Carrie, don't bother me any more. Go now and get packed. You can take the night train. When you return, we'll never mention this again, you understand?

CARRIE. I'll go. (*She starts to go out the door.*)

MRS. LARUE. Carrie, would you please ask Sybil to find me that green album with the snapshots we took of Howay at the beach last summer?

CARRIE. I'll ask her. Good-bye, Mrs. Larue. (*Slowly and sadly Carrie goes up the stairs and out of the door.*)

BOY. Mother, I'm afraid the Loomis girls were offended with you.

MRS. LARUE. (*She stares at him again as though he were a stranger.*) Oh—were they? I'm sorry.

BOY. Isn't it time to change for dinner, Mother?

MRS. LARUE. I don't seem to be hungry, Howay. The cook will bring your dinner to your room. You don't mind?

BOY. Oh no, Mother. Whatever you say.

MRS. LARUE. (*She goes to him now and kisses him lightly on the forehead.*) Good night, dear. Sleep well.

BOY. (*On his way to the door, he turns and looks at her*

39

directly in the eyes. His voice is low.) Like a log, Mother.

> (*He goes out and she watches him climb the long stairs. Then she looks at the oil painting. When the door has closed on the* BOY, *she rushes to the telephone and quickly picks up the receiver. She dials hurriedly.*)

MRS. LARUE. Operator! Operator! This is Mrs. Howard V. Larue speaking at Marchville 19903. I got a call about five minutes ago. Could you trace it for me? I would like to know exactly where it came from? Oh— you say that's impossible! Thank you——

> (SYBIL *now enters the room carrying a green album in her arms.*)

MRS. LARUE (*runs and grabs the album from* SYBIL *quickly*). Oh, I beg your pardon, Sybil. Thank you. (*She opens the album and looks intently at the snapshots inside. Suddenly she snaps it shut.*) Sybil, I—I believe I shall drive into town tonight. I want you to go with me. We'll have to take Howay with us since Carrie is leaving. Tell Nelson to order the car and don't, please don't, say anything to Carrie about this. She's going away and let's not bother her.

> (MRS. LARUE *turns and looks out of the windows toward the Blue, Blue Mountains. But it has grown darker and now she cannot see them. She goes slowly up the stairs.* SYBIL, *a puzzled frown on her face, watches her.*

> *Slowly the curtain comes down on* Scene One.)

ACT ONE

SCENE 2

THE TIME: *It is about an hour after the curtain of scene one. Night.*

THE SET: *The Shantyland Pool Hall Lunchroom in the very worst section of town.*

As the curtain rises we see first a man in a white chef's cap and apron standing and looking out at us from an opening in the wall. There is a shelf before him. He is standing in the kitchen and when he gets an order he places the food on the shelf. Then the waiter comes and gets it and takes it in another part of the lunchroom which we cannot see.

There are a few tables and chairs on the stage. There are old packing boxes against the wall. There is dust in the corner and a few old papers on the floor. It is not a very clean place.

At the left side of the stage is a door. On this door are painted the words: "Boss's Office. Keep Out."

Smoke curls from the kitchen, out through the opening where the chef stands and out through the window.

At the back there is a door which leads to the main part of the lunchroom and through which the waiter always leaves and enters. And at the right side of the stage a door which leads to the street outside. This door is now open. A big old cat pokes her nose inside— sniffs and then goes out again. Perhaps her nose has told her this is a strange place probably full of gangsters and she wants no part of them.

The CHEF, *whose name is Ellsworth, is a jolly-look-*
ing fat man. Although we can see him only from the
waist up, what he is now doing looks interesting
enough and it is something we see few grown people
doing in public. He is playing the piano on the shelf.
There are no piano keys on this shelf and yet he is
playing like an expert. He plays the bass notes on the
bass side of the shelf and the treble notes on the treble
side. He sometimes crosses his hands. When the music
he hears pleases him, he smiles. When he strikes a
wrong note he frowns. We can hear the sound of
bacon and hamburgers sizzling in the kitchen behind
him.

There enters from the back door a waiter wearing
a black jacket with tails and a white apron tied around
his middle. He is young and brown-haired. He loves
music. He looks at the CHEF, *sees that he is playing*
the piano and then he begins to do dance steps. He
looks at the pad he is carrying. There is a pencil stuck
behind one ear.

VIRGIL. (*He calls out as he dances.*) One bowl of chili.

CHEF. Who wants it?

VIRGIL. A customer out in the lunchroom—who do you
think?

CHEF. What's the name of the customer wants the bowl
of chili.

VIRGIL. I didn't get his name—but he's wearing a polka
dot tie.

CHEF. You know me—I want to know his name. Go back
and get it.

    (VIRGIL *goes back through the door into the lunch-*
    room.

And now the lights in the Shantyland Lunchroom
go out and we see the street outside. It is dark
and dreary, littered with old cans full of waste
paper and the street lamp in the distance glitters
only faintly. We can see the outside of the lunchroom and the faded sign above the door which
says: "Shantyland."

Down this street we now see MRS. LARUE, NELSON,
SYBIL *and the* STICK BOY. *The* STICK BOY *is wearing a neat little coat, his black hat and his
white gloves. His mother is wearing a small black
hat, black silk dress and carrying a big purse.*
SYBIL *wears a green coat.*
*They walk slowly. They all look tired. It is apparent
they have been walking for a long time.)*

NELSON (*stops and speaks to* MRS. LARUE). We're running around in circles, Mrs. Larue. We been down
this street before.

MRS. LARUE (*looking to the left*). See down there—a half
block. There's a little place by that alley. Let's try
that.

NELSON. We better be careful down here. This is a pretty
tough neighborhood.

MRS. LARUE. Here, take my rings and my wallet. I don't
care what happens, I must find this place.

NELSON. If you only had a little better idea of the place
you're looking for.

SYBIL. I saw a man back there. He looked like he was took
away but he didn't look like he was brought back.

STICK. Mother, it's twenty minutes past my bedtime. My
joints are creaking.

MRS. LARUE. I know. I know. But I had to bring you.
There was no one at home to leave you with as long
as Carrie was going away. Let's try that other corner,
down at the end of this block.

(*They go off the stage toward the other corner. The
lights now go up in the lunchroom again.* VIRGIL
is standing by the CHEF's *window.*)

VIRGIL. Okay, I got the name.

44

CHEF. (*He is playing.*) Wait—listen! What tune am I playing? (*He thumps with his fingers hard on the shelf. We hear a sound like the pattering of rain drops in rhythm.*)

VIRGIL. Do the bass. (*He listens as the* CHEF *does the bass.*) Is it *Melancholy Baby?*

CHEF. (*How angry this makes him!*) No, dope. Listen harder. (*He plays more.*)

VIRGIL. That's what I hear—*Melancholy Baby.*

CHEF. What I'm playing and what you're hearing are not necessarily the same. Get with me—will you?

VIRGIL. Is it *Margie?*

CHEF. You didn't listen. I am playing *Ah, Sweet Mystery of Life.*

VIRGIL. You were not. You're playing *Margie* and you're only saying you were playing the other one.

CHEF. Prove it. Well—what do you want?

VIRGIL. The customer for the chili is named Lancelot K. Mehaffey of Green River, Wyoming.

CHEF. (*Dreamily he leans his chin on his palm.*) Lancelot K. Mehaffey! Green River, Wyoming! That's pretty. That sends me. For a name like that I would love to dish up a bowl of chili.
  (*He pushes a bowl of chili out onto the shelf.*
  VIRGIL *takes the chili and is about to deliver it to the customer. But he thinks of something else, comes back to the shelf and lowers his voice, first looking around in a mysterious manner.*)

VIRGIL. Where—are the boys tonight?

CHEF. They went off on a bank job, and the boss went off on one of his own. I know better than to ask the boss

45

questions. Where he went is for him to know and me to find out. (*He begins to play again and* VIRGIL *begins to dance.*) Say, you, quit that dancing. Get to work. I hear somebody out there calling a waiter.

(*The door from the street opens and now we see entering two strange characters,* DIRTY JOE *and the* STINKER. DIRTY JOE *is a small fellow in a long black overcoat, white tennis shoes with no shoe-laces, a necktie but no shirt. He carries 'in his hand a pair of yellow gloves held together by a safety pin. He fancies that he dresses well. No one has ever told him anything different. He is a happy little man. But there is something else about him. He has one hand in a menacing fash-ion in one pocket as though he held a gun.*

The STINKER *is a tall fellow, much younger. His suit fits him too tightly. His trousers are too short. His hat is too small. He wears one red sock and one blue one. He has figured that this is a kind of dis-guise and that the cops will not catch him. To-night the* STINKER *looks somewhat unhappy. He goes over and sits on one of the empty boxes and stares into space.*)

JOE (*to the* CHEF). Hi-ya, Ellsworth!

CHEF. Hi-ya, Joe. Hi-ya, Stinker.

STINKER. Ahhhhhhhhhhhhhhhhhhhhhhhhhhhhhhhhhhh—shadup!

CHEF. Okay (*to* JOE *in a whisper*). How did it go—the bank job?

JOE. (*He is disgusted.*) We couldn't even get in. The bank was closed. It's a holiday.

CHEF. Say, let me tell you somethin'—— (*He is about to*

46

let him in on the fact that banks are usually closed on holidays when VIRGIL *enters from the lunchroom.*)

VIRGIL. Fellow named Looty from Sioux Falls, South Dakota, wants to know if he can have ham on rye or cheese on white?

CHEF. Looty—Looty—that is a big sissy name. No, and furthermore go back and take the oyster crackers and the salt and pepper and the table cloth off the table where he is (*under his breath*). Looty—Looty—it's sickening! (VIRGIL *with a sigh goes back to do this. He had rather liked the man Looty himself and besides he looked hungry. The* CHEF *now turns to* JOE.) Joe, what's the matter with the Stinker. He seems low to-night.

JOE. The Stinker is losing his nerve.

STINKER (*gets off the packing box. His jaw is firm. His eyes glitter. He looks hard at* JOE). Say that again!

JOE. (*He is very calm.*) The Stinker is losing his nerve.

STINKER. (*He now takes a notebook and a long pencil from his pocket. He licks the end of the pencil with his tongue.*) That's twice you said that. I'm keeping count. (*He writes it in the notebook and puts it back in his pocket.*)

JOE. You know how the Stinker is always goin' around town lookin' for an old lady to push under a street car?

CHEF. It's all he talks about. He is a bore on the subject.

STINKER (*his eyes gleaming*). Clang, clang, clang—here comes the car! Push her under—I dream about it—it's music—it's rhythm.

47

CHEF. You talk about it, sure—all talk. But have you done it yet—no!

STINKER. I'm tryin', ain't I? I get A. for effort, don't I?

JOE. He's tryin'. But when he catches a street car there's no old ladies, and when he catches an old lady, there's no street car. He needs a break.

CHEF. What I can't figure is why you want to push some old lady under a street car?

STINKER. Why, for a laugh, you dope!

(*We hear in the distance the sound of coughing from someone coming up the street.*)

CHEF. Jiggers, boys—it's the boss. His cough has personality.

(*They immediately all get busy. The* CHEF *gets busy wiping off the shelf with a dish towel and the* STINKER *and* JOE *get busy putting fierce tough expressions on their faces. Here in Shantyland, everybody who works for the boss, must work. And when they are not working they must have looks on their faces which will show how they will look when they are working.*

Enter the boss. He is POISON EDDIE SCHELLENBACH. *And he looks exactly like what he is—a gangster boss. He wears a gray derby hat, a checked gray suit, a beautiful red shirt and a beautiful orange tie. Tonight he must have something important on his mind. He is frowning. He walks across the stage, looking neither to the left nor right, kicks open the door of his office with the toe of his shoe and goes inside. The boys and the* CHEF *look uneasy.*)

48

CHEF. (*He hopes the boss is not sore at him.*) Boys, don't the boss look swell?

> (*But before they can answer, the boss has flung open the door of his office again. He strides across the stage with long steps.*)

EDDIE. (*He stares at them fiercely.*) How wah yuh, boys? Don't answer. (*He puts his right hand inside his coat pocket and we all know what that means with a gangster.*) The cops are out like flies. I'm hotter than a firecracker but they can't prove a thing. There's ice in this town but it's all behind plate glass. I've cased this burg from end to end and all I bring home is alibis. What's on the agenda? (*He sits at a chair behind one of the tables, pounds the table.*) Call a meeting! Call a meeting!

STINKER. That's what I'm gonna do. I'm gonna call a meeting.

EDDIE. Call it then and don't just stand there sayin' you're gonna call it—call it.

STINKER. I'm not gonna just stand here sayin' I'm gonna call it—I'm gonna call it. (*Puts fingers in his mouth and whistles.*) I called it.

> (JOE *and the* STINKER *now sit down on the empty packing boxes half way across the stage from the boss because of course they are not permitted to sit at the same table with him.*)

EDDIE (*looking very stern*). Boys, the question before us at this meeting is this one: Do we take this boy we call the squirt out of the dish washing department and promote him to the mobster department? (JOE *raises his hand like a school boy in class.*) Dirty Joe Mc-

Ginnis, I see your hand up.

JOE (*stands beside his packing box*). Boss, I would like
to put to us a question concerning the boy we call the
squirt. What do we know about him and is any of it
good? I would like to remind ourselves that he is prac-
tically a stranger to us, having lived here in the bosom
of us only a matter of three weeks, which reckoned
against the life span of life is a mere drop of water—
or spit—I SHOULD say. (*He sits down.*)

EDDIE. What Dirty Joe has put, he has put good. What
do we know about this kid? Only that one night about
three weeks ago he ran in here on the lam from a cop
who was chasing him. We hid him out until the cop
had left, which anybody would do naturally. We don't
live to make life easy for cops—eh, boys? (*Make life
easy for cops—never! They all sneer and laugh loudly.*)
Shaddup! But this kid had the nerve to stand up and
tell us he come from out there in some swell neighborhood on the Van Tyne Road. Any kid that can tell a
big lie like that has got something we can use in our
business, and business is not so good right about now.
Am I right? Or do you guys want to tangle with me?
(*He menaces them with hand in pocket again.*)

JOE (*seeing the boss's hand inside the pocket of his
coat*). The boss is right.

STINKER. (*He looks at the hand inside the coat, too.*)
The boss is always right.

EDDIE. Sure, I'm right.

JOE. But what else did this kid do beside break a street
lamp?

STINKER. This kid is a cream puff.

JOE. The Stinker had to work around here for three years

50

before he was took into the mob. But this squirt has been here only three weeks. Oh, what hot air he peddles! He was tryin' to tell me the other day he has a pony, a swan boat—all slush! Slush!

EDDIE. (*He has been lost in thought. Now he rises.*) Look! You take your average A number one confidence man and he always starts life that way; big dreams, with his fond memories away ahead of him! Now, for the last time, I will hear from the Stinker. I want you to vote—yes—no.

STINKER. I can't vote yes—I wouldn't vote no.

JOE. I say this kid is a cream puff.

EDDIE (*pushes* JOE *in the face again*). Stinker, for the last time, I will hear from you!

STINKER. I . . . vote he is a cream puff.

EDDIE (*pounding the table*). Vote—vote—take him in don't take him in. (*Hand on gun in pocket, he marches toward them. They pick up the empty packing boxes in their hands to ward off his attack.*) I said VOTE.
(*As they are backing away from the boss's anger and as he continues to pursue them into a corner, the door from the street opens and some one enters. It is a little old woman. She is wearing a black shawl over a housedress, a small black hat with one faded silk flower sticking up from the brim. Her shoes are heavy black oxfords. Her expression is stern. This is* MRS. SCHELLENBACH, *the boss's mother. She places her hands on her hips and calls out.*)

THE BOSS'S MOTHER. Edward Arthur Schellenbach!
(*At the sound of her voice, the boss grows pale and*

51

stands very still. DIRTY JOE *and the* STINKER *flatten themselves against the wall and hide their faces behind the packing boxes, hoping she will not see them.*)

EDDIE. Yes, Mama! Hello, Mama!

(*She walks over to him and, raising her hand, gives him a stinging slap on the back of the neck. He puts up his hands but she clouts him again with a "Take this" and a "Take that" expression on her face.*)

THE BOSS'S MOTHER. Where did you sleep last night?

EDDIE. I was with the fellas, Mama.

BOSS'S MOTHER. You straighten up. Don't slouch.

EDDIE. Sure, Ma.

BOSS'S MOTHER. And tie those shoe lacings.

EDDIE. You bet, Ma.

(*He leans over to tie his shoelaces and she gives him a swift kick. As she starts to walk out of the lunchroom,* JOE *peeks from behind the packing box. He makes his voice polite and sweet.*)

JOE. Nice day, Mrs. Schellenbach! (*She glares at him.*)

STINKER. How do, Mrs. Schellenbach!

BOSS'S MOTHER (*looks up at the* STINKER *who is so much bigger than she is*). You—bend down. (*As he bends down she gives him a clout on the ear. She turns now to her son.*) You be in early tonight and don't bring any of these bums home with you. (*Then with a hard stamping sound she walks out and slams the door.*)

(*The boss is holding the side of his face. He looks dazed. He turns and stares at his mob.*)

EDDIE. Where were we?

52

JOE. The vote—the vote.

EDDIE (*still dazed*). Yeah—the vote—the vote——
(*But now there is a knock at the outside door.
STINKER goes over to answer it. EDDIE looks frightened. He is wondering if his mother has come
back.
In the doorway we see* MRS. LARUE. *She looks up at
the tall* STINKER, *having to bend her head way
back.*)

MRS. LARUE. I'm sorry to bother you but do you know of
a place around here called something like the Shantyland Pool Hall Lunch?

STINKER. Yeah!

MRS. LARUE. (*She turns to* NELSON *who is standing behind her.*) Nelson, he knows—he knows. At last—at
last—our search is over. (*She looks at the* STINKER
again.) Would you be good enough to tell me where
it is, please?

STINKER. Naw!

MRS. LARUE. (*To* NELSON) He knows but he won't tell.
I never heard of such a thing in all my life. Come on,
Nelson—Sybil—Howay—we'll find some one who is
more cooperative. (*She steps out of the doorway but
the* STICK BOY *now appears there. He looks at the*
STINKER *with disgust. The* STINKER *looks down at him.*)

STICK BOY. You are very rude. You should be ashamed!
(*The* STINKER *is not ashamed but he is ready. He gives
the* STICK BOY *a big hefty push. The* STICK BOY *runs
calling*) Mother, Mother, he hit me—he hit me! (*He
runs away bawling loudly.*)

JOE. The vote—the vote——

EDDIE. Ah yes, the vote about the kid. We have to agree —that's the rule of the mob. And if we don't agree on this kid I'm liable to have to boot him out into the street. He eats too much for the work he's doin'.

JOE. Before we vote, Boss, I would like to tell you this. We should not take that kid into our mob because there is something inside that kid which considers himself better than we are.

EDDIE (*very angry. He grabs* JOE *by the lapels*). What's that? Did he say that? It will go hard with him from me if he said that!

JOE. Naw, he didn't say it—but I get it. It comes to me and I get it and I'm givin' it to you.

EDDIE. Better than we are! Tell you what. We'll be smart. We'll hide here and take another look at him when he's not watchin'. Hey, Ellsworth—— (*He goes over and leans across the shelf into the kitchen. The* CHEF *appears at the opening.*) Send that kid out here and don't say nothin'.

(JOE *and the* STINKER *flatten themselves against the wall at stage right so they cannot be seen.*)

CHEF. The kid is busy washin' dishes, Boss. It's our rush hour. But if you say so, I'll send him out. (*He turns and calls.*) Hey, squirt, take the tray and work the lunchroom.

(*Now onto the stage from the door of the kitchen there appears a small blonde boy about nine years old. And as we look at him we realize that Mrs. McThing did a very good job with the Stick Boy she left for Mrs. Larue at Larue Towers. Because the Stick Boy is an exact copy of this one in the shape of ears, nose, mouth, head, weight, height*

54

and coloring. But that's all. This boy, who is the real Howay Larue has tousled hair and a smudge of dirt on his cheek. There is a button off his shirt and a rip in his blue jeans. His hands are grimy and there is one shoe without a shoelace.)

HOWAY. (*He has tied a white apron around his middle and picked up a tray. He walks to the chef's shelf. He does not see the gangsters who are watching him. He speaks to the* CHEF.) Ellsworth, has anyone been around here asking for me?

CHEF. Who you expectin'?

HOWAY. Oh—somebody!

CHEF. Who?

HOWAY. Just some one.

CHEF. Just some one—who's that?

HOWAY. Oh—nobody.

CHEF. That's just who was here. Nobody.

(HOWAY *looks disappointed. But he must get to work anyway, so he takes his tray and goes to the back of the room where the waiter always goes and enters the main part of the lunchroom which we do not see, where he will walk up to strange people, take a pad and pencil and say things like, "What's your order, Mister," or "What'll it be for you, lady?"*

After he has gone out, the gangsters come out of their corner.)

EDDIE. (*He is grinning.*) See, the kid didn't say who he was expectin'. I like that. He's close-mouthed.

JOE. It could be dumbness. Maybe he didn't *know* who

he was expectin'.

EDDIE. Shhh—get back, here he comes—back.

HOWAY. Chef, the guy's name was De Witt de Ferdestellar from Keokuk and he wanted a hot roast beef sandwich, but I knew you wouldn't like that name and I told him we were out of roast beef and he better change his name or go to another lunchroom. He went out.

CHEF. Thanks, bud—you're my pal! De Witt Ferdestellar oh—oh! How terrible.

(HOWAY *has gone out through the back door again into the lunchroom. The gangsters again come out of hiding and hold their heads together.*)

EDDIE. That kid is sharp. Didja hear how sharp he is? He knows our chef and that saves time and time is money.

JOE. I still say he is a panty waist.

STINKER. Shhh, here he comes again. Get back.
(*They hide again.*)

HOWAY (*enters calling out gaily*). One roast chicken for Duane B. Wilson of Alamosa, Colorado, by the Singing Sand Dunes.

CHEF (*handing him a plate with a large roast chicken on it*). Now that is a real order and that is a name with real class. Give him my best regards.

(*But after* HOWAY *has taken the plate with the chicken and started to walk with it, the chicken falls off the plate and onto the floor.* HOWAY *looks down at it. He looks around carefully. He sees nobody watching him. So he picks the chicken off the floor quickly and, since there is dust on the*

*side of it, he spits on it and wipes it against the
side of his pants and puts it back on the plate. At
this point with a loud whoop the gangsters come
out of hiding.* HOWAY's *face turns pale as he sees
the boss walking toward him. Gee, he is caught!*)

EDDIE. Okay, kid, I seen you—I seen what you done.

HOWAY (*paler still. What will happen to him now? The
boss did see him wipe off a roast chicken on his pants*).
Mr. Schellenbach!

EDDIE. (*He is extending his hand to* HOWAY.) You have
passed the test, kid. You're in—congrats—shake!

HOWAY. (*He is so surprised. Then the boss is not angry.
Why not?*) Thanks, Mr. Schellenbach, thanks a lot. I

know I should have gone back to the kitchen for a clean chicken—but——

STINKER (*picks the boy up in the air*). Shhh, don't spoil it. You didn't and that's what counts.

JOE. I was against you, kid—but you came through—you're not a panty waist. You're one of us.

EDDIE. (*He has seated himself grandly at his own table.*) Squirt! I have some big news for you. Scram, boys. I will talk to this kid alone. (JOE *and the* STINKER *do not move.*) I said scram—SCRAM!

STINKER. That's what we're gonna do—we're gonna scram.

EDDIE. Scram then and don't just stand there sayin' you're gonna scram—SCRAM!

STINKER. We're not gonna just stand here, sayin' we're gonna scram—we're gonna scram. (*They rush out of the door fast.*)

EDDIE. Sit down, kid. (HOWAY *comes over and starts to sit in a chair at the same table with the boss. But the boss frowns, points to the boxes.*) Not here—over there. Don't try to move in too fast. (HOWAY *goes over and sits on the packing boxes across the stage from* POISON EDDIE.) Now, kid—this here is your lucky day. We have just voted to take you out of the dish washin' department and promote you to the mobster shift. From now on, kid, you are workin' with me and the boys.

HOWAY. (*His face lights up with pleasure.*) Really—oh swell! (*Then he remembers something. He sighs with disappointment.*) Oh gosh—oh darn!

EDDIE. What's the matter?

HOWAY. Well, you see, Mr. Schellenbach, I wish I could

58

—but I can't. I was finally able to get my mother on the phone tonight so she'll be along to get me any minute now, and take me back home with her.

EDDIE. (*A storm cloud has been gathering over his face.*) Your mother! Take you back home with her? Oh no, kid, nobody goes back from here—lots go down, and a few go up—but nobody goes back. So—you can't be in the mob. Your mother wants you. Maybe my mother wants me, too. I've got a notion to rub you out right now! (*He puts his right hand into his right coat pocket.*)

HOWAY. But Mr. Schellenbach, I've certainly had a big time here. I think you're just about the toughest man I ever met in my whole life. (EDDIE *grins. He is pleased to hear this.*) But you don't know my mother.

EDDIE. Afraid of your mother? Afraid of your mother? I got no use for people afraid of their mother. Joe was right. You are a cream puff.

HOWAY. No I'm not, Mr. Schellenbach, but my mother always carries on so about me. I'm an only child and she says I am all she has. I don't know why she says it but she does. But if you'll make me the same offer when I'm eighteen, I'll join the mob.

EDDIE. (*He is angry at him. His pride is hurt, too.*) Back to work—earn your keep—you disgust me. Cream puff—panty waist—get out of here or I'll slug you. Beat it—NOW!

(HOWAY *runs back into the kitchen.*
At this point, while the boss is walking back and forth in anger, not noticing the door leading to the street, it opens slowly and there enters into the room the same little ragged girl we saw at Larue

59

Towers. She is carrying the toy train we saw her pick up there. On tiptoe she starts hurrying back in the direction of the kitchen where HOWAY *has gone. This is* MIMI MCTHING.)

EDDIE. Hey you—not so fast—where do you think you're goin'? (MIMI *stops. She says nothing.*) Come here. (*She walks over to him.*) Who are you? I axed you. Who are you?

MIMI. Me? They hung the big round moon up there for me to look at. When birds sing in the trees they sing for me and no one else. The grass grows just for me to walk on. I am a dear little white rose—the loveliest child in the whole wide world.

EDDIE. Yeah? Who was tellin' you?

MIMI. My mother.

EDDIE. Your mother? Always these mothers! Kid, let me give you a little advice. (*He walks over to give her the advice. She has to lean her head way back to look up at him because he is a very tall man, and she is a small girl.* EDDIE *looks down at her. He sighs sadly. He wonders if she is worth the trouble he is about to take with her.*) Kid, let me give you a little advice. You can't believe the kind of baloney your mother puts out. Now me—take me—I'm a mobster. (*He puts his thumbs in the lapels of his coat and walks back and forth and he says, "I am a mobster," in the same tone with which some people might say, "I won the first prize."*) I am Poison Eddie Schellenbach, but do you know what my mother called me? (MIMI *shakes her head. She has no idea what* EDDIE's *mother called him.*) She always called me her little apple dumpling. Take a good look at me, kid. Look me over carefully. Don't hurry, take your

60

time. Start with my shoes and go on up. (*She does this.*) Now, do I look like anybody's little apple dumpling? (MIMI *nods her heads slowly. She has looked him over carefully and the resemblance between Poison* EDDIE *and an apple dumpling seems to her to be quite striking. But* EDDIE *does not agree. A look of disgust spreads across his face. He is a mobster, not an apple dumpling.*) Ahh—get glasses! You don't see good. Kid, this is a cruel world and it behooves us not to go around blabbing what our mother calls us. There's other people looking at that moon and hearin' birds and walkin' on grass and they're not gonna like it when you claim it's all for you. Out of annoyance they are liable to step on your face. Now, let's try it again—WHO—ARE—YOU?

MIMI. I am Mimi. A dear little white rose, the loveliest child in the whole wide world.

EDDIE. (*He's getting more and more disgusted with her.*) Naw! Naw! You don't catch on, do you? Look, suppose somebody—well, cops maybe—say to me, "You —who are you?" And I say, "Me, why I am Mrs. Schellenbach's little apple dumpling." Do you know what they would do? (MIMI *shakes her head. She does not know. She does not know any cops. She is not interested in cops.*) They would stir up my face like an omelet. That apple dumpling line would make any cop—even a private eye—fly into a rage, see?

MIMI. (*She is stating a fact. She is speaking with the same tone she would use if she were to say, "two times two makes four."*) I am a dear little white rose.

EDDIE. (*He walks away from her. It is obvious now that she will never learn.*) Aw, skip it. Your ma has sold

62

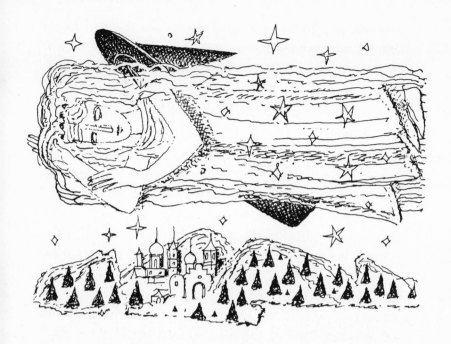

you a line and you have bought every bit of it.

MIMI. My mother is Mrs. McThing.

EDDIE. Mrs. McThing! Seems to me I have heard that handle before some place. She ever been in police court?

MIMI. Where?

EDDIE. Police court—a popular rendezvous for an exclusive few. What is Mrs. McThing's racket?

MIMI. (*These are strange words—police court—racket— what is this big man talking about?*) What?

EDDIE. What does she do? How does she live?

MIMI. (*She tiptoes over to him, takes his hand in hers and starts to pull him toward a window.*) Shhh—up there in the Blue, Blue Mountains, there is a big dark woods, and my mother—— (*But as she is about to tell* EDDIE *all about her mother, Mrs. McThing,* HOWAY *comes in, sees her and runs to her.*)

HOWAY. Mimi—hey, Mimi——

EDDIE. Is this conceited little character a pal of yours?

HOWAY. Well, she likes to play with me.

EDDIE. I have nothing against her so far, but it gives the place a sissy name for kids to be running in and out with toys, so maybe she better—— (*He makes a motion of his hand that* MIMI *should go home.*)

HOWAY. Oh, Mr. Schellenbach, don't send her home. Come here, let me whisper something to you. (*He whispers something in* EDDIE's *ear.*)

EDDIE. (*He looks at* MIMI *again.*) So—she says her old lady is a witch! So what! This neighborhood is full of witches—two of them livin' next door to me—and one in the basement and lots upstairs.

> (HOWAY *is now looking at* MIMI *with a new light in his eyes. If witches are as ordinary as* EDDIE *has said, then* MIMI *is not half so unusual as she has pretended to be.*)

MIMI. (*She levels her forefinger sternly at* EDDIE.) If you send me home, I will turn you into a cuspidor.

EDDIE. (*It has never occurred to him at any time in his life that he would ever be threatened with this. The prospect annoys him.*) What is she hanging around here for, anyway. Is that what she goes around doin' to people?

HOWAY. I hate to say it, Mr. Schellenbach, but she is hanging around here because—well, she likes me.

EDDIE. Likes you? Well, kid, don't be too sad about

that. I have been in the same situation myself with bigger dames and there is no cure for it but death. A witch—that don't scare me none, but a dame that likes me—that is murder! (*turns to* MIMI). Behave yourself, kid, and we won't bother you much. But if you go interfering with business around here, out you go! And you leave our cuspidors alone, too. (*He goes into his office.*)

MIMI (*now hands* HOWAY *the train*). Here. I brought this for you. I like you. (*She puts her arms around him.*)

HOWAY (*pulls away. He does not like this*). No slush, Mimi. You went to my house, did you see my mother? Did you talk to her?

MIMI. No. But I sat on the wall. I saw a boy riding your pony.

HOWAY. A boy—what boy? (*His eyes grow wide. He cannot believe this news.*) You're a meat head, Mimi. My mother wouldn't let any boy but me ride my pony. You're making this up.

MIMI. She helped him get up on the pony. I saw her. That boy looks just like you. My mother made him. She put him into your bed the night you went away. She has magic, my mother. She put this stick boy into your bed.

HOWAY. (*He still cannot believe.*) But what is the matter with my mother letting this stick ride my pony?

MIMI. She likes him. He is so clean. He has books all the time. He minds. He is always please and thank you and excuse me. Old hens were there—pish—pash—cut-a-cutt-a-cutt cut——

65

HOWAY. The Loomis girls—those drips!

MIMI. They kissed him. He kissed them——

HOWAY. This boy kissed those drips? He must be a drip, too.

MIMI. Your mother kissed him, too. I saw her. She patted his hair. She called him honey pie.

HOWAY. (*This news shocks him deeply.*) Honey pie! She always called me that stinking pet name! She called HIM that? (*Much as he disliked the name, the idea of his own mother using it for another boy he simply cannot believe. He hated it, but it was his.*) This drippy boy? This stick? My mother called him that? Oh, wait till I get home. I'll clean him.

MIMI. You can't go home. You can't get in. They don't let anybody in.

HOWAY. (*He wipes angry tears from his eyes.*) Okay— skip it. If she likes that drip—let her have him. She can keep him. See if I care.

> (*He sits on a box and* MIMI *comes and sits beside him as the lights go out. There are angry tears in his eyes. But there would be no tears in* HOWAY'S *eyes if he knew what we can now see in the street outside. We see his mother and* SYBIL *again walking down the street. If* HOWAY *only knew that his mother was walking every inch of every square block in the neighborhood trying to find him, he would get up off the old box and rush out into the street. But he has no way of seeing through the walls. And we in the audience who know all of this, cannot step up and tell him.*
>
> MRS. LARUE *is talking to* SYBIL. *She is beginning to*

66

*get tired from searching and her walk is slower
than it was when we saw her before. She has ap-
parently left the* STICK BOY *with* NELSON *in the
Larue limousine down the block. If she knew
that her boy—her own boy—the real boy, was at
this very minute sitting inside the building she is
passing, she would joyfully run inside. But she
does not know this and so she walks right by the
Shantyland Pool Hall Lunchroom.*)

MRS. LARUE. If I'd only listened more carefully. If I'd
only written it down. What was it he said?

SYBIL. Who told you about this place, Mrs. Larue?

LARUE. Who? Well, I'm not quite sure.

SYBIL. You're lookin' for a place you don't know the name
of, or where it is, or who told you? Well, if you don't
know what you're lookin' for—then it makes no difference if we don't find it.

MRS. LARUE. Oh yes, it does, Sybil. It does——

SYBIL. Sometimes when you don't know what you're
lookin' for, you find somethin' you don't like—that's
life.
(*They walk down the street and out of our sight.
The lights now come on again inside the lunchroom.*)

MIMI. (*She is patting* HOWAY's *hand.*) Dear child, don't
be sad. Here, you can play with me. At home you
can't play with me. Your mother won't let you. So, be
joyful—let's play.

HOWAY. If I was just a little bigger I could join the navy.
Next year I will join—see if I don't.

67

MIMI. (*She is so fond of this boy.*) I will join the navy, too.

HOWAY. Don't be a cornball. You're a girl. They wouldn't take you.

MIMI. If they won't take me—I won't take them. They started it.

> (*At this moment* JOE *and* STINKER *come in running. They are very excited. Their eyes are glistening. They are breathing rapidly. They call loudly: "Boss! Boss!"*)

EDDIE (*runs out of his office*). What's up?

JOE. Boss—down at the corner—there is a beautiful big car—with a chauffeur—and a dame——

HOWAY. My mother—she's come for me—good-bye mob! (*He starts for the door.*)

STINKER. The dame's hair—it's long and gold and blowing in the wind. It is so long it got caught on a telegraph pole a whole block behind. We had to help unwrap it and carry it up to her——

> (HOWAY *stops at the door. This is not his mother. His shoulders slump.*)

JOE. And the chauffeur looked like a big brown bear.

MIMI (*happily*). My mother—my mother! (*She runs out.*)

JOE. And this dame has got an armful of red roses.

STINKER. And she was smiling—she smiled at me——

JOE. And with every smile she threw—she threw a rose with it. We got one for you, boss.

EDDIE. Thanks. If there is anything in this lousy world I love—it's a red, red rose for free. Did you look at the license plate. I wonder if this is somebody I know.

68

STINKER. She looked like a movie queen—a glamorous witch.

HOWAY (*slowly*). That is Mimi's old lady and she can have her. And you can have her, too. And you can have your own old lady, too. And my old lady, too. She can take a long jump for herself—into a lake with that stick—for all I care. (*He turns aside so they will not see the tears in his eyes.*)

EDDIE. Squirt—what did you say? (*He walks slowly to* HOWAY *after exchanging a look with the boys.*)

HOWAY. Mr. Schellenbach—I changed my mind—my mother doesn't want me after all. I would like to join the mob.

STINKER and JOE. He can't change his mind. It's too late. He's a cream puff.

EDDIE. Shut up. Did you guys just hear what this kid said about his mother? That takes nerve. This is a kid I could learn to like. (*He throws his arms around* HOWAY's *shoulders.*) Okay, kid, you are in the mob—shake—mobster!

> (*But* STINKER *and* JOE *are not yet in agreement about this boy. Again they yell, "He's a panty waist—we don't want him in the mob."*

> HOWAY *turns and looks at them with scorn. He is not afraid of anything now. He walks with a tough slouch to the two mobsters, stands facing them and says, "Ahhhhhhhhhhhh—shaddup," as the* CURTAIN *comes down.*)

ACT ONE

SCENE 3

THE SET: *The Shantyland Pool Hall Lunchroom.*

THE TIME: *A few minutes after the curtain of scene two. We see the* CHEF *playing the piano on his shelf. There is no one else in the room and he is smiling dreamily as he crosses his hands, plays grace notes and runs—or at least so he thinks. There is one thing we shall never know—no matter how long we live. We shall never know if Ellsworth knows he is* not *playing a real piano. He would never tell anyone. He considers this his own business and of course it is.*

The door at the back—the one leading into the lunchroom proper is opening. Who is this? It is MRS. LARUE. *She is alone. She walks into the room and sniffs as she looks around this shabby back room. She sees the* CHEF *and walks to him.*

MRS. LARUE. Could you possibly tell me if there is a telephone anywhere around here? (*She is standing right by a wall telephone when she asks this question but she does not see it.*)

CHEF (*pointing*). Possibly that one.

MRS. LARUE. Thank you.

    (*She goes to the telephone and dials a number. The* CHEF *continues to play. She listens as her number is ringing.*

    Now coming in from the back door are NELSON *and the* STICK BOY.)

71

STICK BOY. Here she is, Nelson. Mother, we were wondering where you had gone.

MRS. LARUE. (*She is a little annoyed.*) What's the matter? Couldn't you wait in that other room for me?

NELSON. Some tough-looking guys in there were giving him dirty looks, ma'am. I thought we better leave.

STICK. Oh Mother, they were such awful looking people—no neckties!

MRS. LARUE. I thought I would call Evva Loomis but the line is busy. She has a friend who is a social worker. They go into these neighborhoods all of the time. I'll try her again in a minute. She is so long-winded on the telephone. We better wait here.
(*She goes over to a table and sits down. The* STICK BOY *and* NELSON *sit down with her.*
VIRGIL *comes in. He goes to* CHEF's *window.*)

VIRGIL. Hot roast beef san for ex convict number 9999999.

CHEF. Jinx Maloney. (*He puts out the sandwich and* VIRGIL *goes out with it.*)

NELSON. (*He has smelled the hot roast beef.*) Ahh—that smells good.

MRS. LARUE. Would you like one, Nelson?

NELSON. I wouldn't mind.

MRS. LARUE (*to the* STICK BOY *who is sitting stiff and straight at the table, his hands folded primly*). What will you have, darling?

STICK BOY. You decide, Mother. You know best.

MRS. LARUE. Isn't there something you'd like? This is a terrible looking place but we have to wait some place. What would you like?

72

STICK BOY. It's not what I would like, Mother. It is whatever you would want me to have.

MRS. LARUE. You used to order everything and three
desserts besides. Please tell me what you would like?
(*She stares at him. She is annoyed with him and there
is something about him which frightens her. Could*

CARRIE *have possibly been right? Well, that is just what she is down in this neighborhood to find out. She must—she simply must—find the boy who called her on the telephone. She sighs.*)

STICK BOY. (*He is never upset even when she speaks to him in a tone of annoyance. He is always patient with her.*) But Mother, I only want what you want me to have.

MRS. LARUE. Oh dear! Haven't I got enough on my mind without your sitting there not knowing? I wanted you to grow up. I wanted you to get some sense. But I didn't expect you to go so far. You never could do anything in moderation, could you?

STICK BOY. I'm sorry, Mother, but whatever you say is right even if it is wrong. Mother knows best.

MRS. LARUE. Milk! I'll get you some milk if I have to think for you. (VIRGIL *has come back into the room.*) Waiter! Waiter! (VIRGIL *comes to the table.*) Can we be served here?

VIRGIL. Maybe. What's your order, lady?

MRS. LARUE. Hot roast beef sandwich and one glass of milk. Please see that the glass is clean.

VIRGIL (*getting out his pad and pencil*). What's the name, please?

MRS. LARUE. The name? Whose name? Yours? I wouldn't know.

VIRGIL. Your name, lady. What is it?

MRS. LARUE. My name. But why should I have to give my name? I'm paying cash. I'm not asking for credit.

VIRGIL. It's our chef, lady. He likes to know people's

74

names. He's quite a personality. Lots of color—interesting though—to some people. He don't interest me none.

MRS. LARUE. How utterly ridiculous. I am Mrs. Howard V. Larue.

STICK BOY. The third.

VIRGIL (*goes to the* CHEF's *window—leans through it and calls out*). Hot roast beef sandwich and one glass milk for Mrs. Howard V. Larue III.

> (*The* CHEF *is so horrified at this he pulls down a wooden shutter over the window with a slam-bang sound.*
>
> VIRGIL *was afraid this would happen. He goes wearily over to* MRS. LARUE. *He tells her they are all out.*)

MRS. LARUE. All out—of what?

VIRGIL. What you ordered, lady.

MRS. LARUE. We'll change the order. What will you have, Nelson?

NELSON. Oh, gimme a piece of cherry pie.

MRS. LARUE. And bring my son a glass of water. Please see that the glass is clean.

VIRGIL. All out.

MRS. LARUE. Oh! What DO you have?

VIRGIL. Nothin', lady. We're all out of everything.

MRS. LARUE. Nonsense! Send me the manager. I want to see the manager.

VIRGIL. I will see if Mr. Schellenbach can see you lady, but he is mostly in a meeting with his boys.

> (VIRGIL *goes in to the boss's office.*)

NELSON. (*He leans across the table and speaks in a low voice to* MRS. LARUE.) I wonder if that's Poison Eddie Schellenbach, the mobster?

STICK BOY. Mobster! Oh Mother, how awful! We'd better leave.

MRS. LARUE. Just listen to that. All of your life you have been crazy about gangsters, reading those comic books, listening to those radio programs. Every time you saw the first star, every time you dropped a penny in a wishing well, every time you saw a load of hay, that was always your wish—to meet gangsters, and now—just listen to you!

STICK BOY. That was silly. I am not silly any more, Mother.

MRS. LARUE. Well I wish you would make up your mind what you are. Then I would know where I am.
(*Now into the room walks* POISON EDDIE *his hand in his gun pocket. Behind him come* DIRTY JOE *and the* STINKER, *their hands also in their gun pockets.* EDDIE *walks directly up to* MRS. LARUE.)

EDDIE. What's your trouble, lady?

MRS. LARUE. I demand to know why we can't be served. We gave an order. Other people are being served. I demand an explanation.

EDDIE. It's our chef. He's a temperamental fellow—like all musicians.

MRS. LARUE. But why should he object to serving me—what's wrong with me?

EDDIE (*looks at her carefully*). Lady, you'd know that a

lot better than I would. You might be terrible and me not catch on to it for five or ten minutes. I only went through the sixth grade.

> (JOE *has gone over to the* STICK *and is looking at him carefully. He is struck by the* STICK BOY's *resemblance to their new mobster. But of course, this boy with the neat suit and hat, has his hair combed so neatly, his face so clean and his shoes laced and tied so perfectly, that* JOE *knows there could not possibly be any connection. But he is amused at the* STICK BOY's *hat. He goes and whispers in* EDDIE's *ear, and nudges the* STINKER *to have a look. They all regard the* STICK BOY *with amusement. Here is a genuine cream puff—a real panty waist.*)

STINKER. Look at him, Boss. For a minute I thought it was our new little trigger man sitting out here with the cash customers. Don't they look alike?

EDDIE. (*He looks now, too.*) Oh, they look sort of alike. But what of it. All kids that age look alike. When I was that age I looked alike.

STINKER. (*He is fascinated with the* STICK's *round hat. He goes over and grabs it off the* STICK's *head.* MRS. LARUE *and* NELSON *look uneasily at each other.*) Hey, look at the hat, Boss. I never seen one like this. (*He puts it on his own head. It is much too small, of course, and he looks very silly. But* EDDIE *and* JOE *look at him and laugh.* JOE *now takes the hat.*)

MRS. LARUE. (*She is very, very angry. She gets up from her chair.*) Give my boy back his hat.

STINKER. Ain't quite through playin' with it, lady.

MRS. LARUE. Nelson, do something. They'll ruin it.

NELSON. (*He is really afraid of these fellows and he doesn't care what happens to the* STICK BOY's *hat, but he does not want to admit this to* MRS. LARUE.) Oh, they'll give it back when they're through, Mrs. Larue. Even big guys like to play sometimes.

STINKER. (*He grabs the hat from* JOE's *head and puts it back on his own.*) It don't fit you, Joe.

JOE. Give it back. (*He tries to take it. They now begin to wrestle and* EDDIE *watches them, smiling fondly. "Boys will be boys," he is thinking.*)

MRS. LARUE (*more and more angry*). Nelson, don't sit there like that. Get Howay's hat at once.

NELSON. (*He must admit it now.*) These fellows are pretty rough, ma'am. Let them have the hat. What's a hat? Maybe we better leave.

EDDIE. Time's up, you guys. Give the sissy kid back his sissy hat.

JOE. His hat? Sure. (*At this point,* JOE *takes his own hat— a very large hat, and pulls it down hard over the* STICK BOY's *head. It comes down over his nose. The* STICK BOY *lets out a loud bellowing and crying.*)

STICK BOY. Oh, Mother—Mother—Mother!

MRS. LARUE. Oh, stop crying! (*She takes the big hat off him.*) Nelson, take Howay home. (*The* STICK BOY *still is bawling loudly as* NELSON *hurries him out of the lunchroom.*)

MRS. LARUE. (*She now faces the gangsters with angry eyes. Her eyes are so stern and so piercing that somehow she reminds them of every strict school teacher they ever had. They begin to back slowly away. She*

78

follows them.) You—I have never seen any of you before in my life and I hope you realize that you have made me feel miserable with your rude treatment of my son. I hope you are thoroughly ashamed of yourselves. I am leaving here utterly depressed and sad.

EDDIE. What's the beef? He's not hurt. He can still walk, can't he?

MRS. LARUE. (*She takes the big hat and pushes it into* EDDIE's *hand. She sniffs haughtily and turns to leave as the door from the street opens and* MIMI MC THING *comes in.* MRS. LARUE, *startled, takes a step back as she sees her.*) You—the little girl I sent home that day! What are you doing here? Did you follow me?

MIMI. I want to play with your boy.

MRS. LARUE (*turns to gangsters*). Does this child belong to one of you? So this is your background, little girl. Well, I'm not surprised.

EDDIE. She don't belong to us. She just blows in here and outta here. (*He speaks now to* MIMI.) Hey, kid, haven't you got a home? Haven't you got a mother?

MRS. LARUE. Yes, and where, may I ask, is your mother— if you have one?
   (*Soft tinkling music begins to play. Where it is coming from no one knows. It sounds like the kind of music which happens when you open a musical box. It comes when* MIMI *speaks of her mother.*)

MIMI. (*She points up.*) My mother—oh—oh. (*And then she holds her skirts just so—like a lady.*) Shhh—away up there—in the Blue, Blue Mountains—where the trees are tall there is a hush, hush, hush. My mother

79

is walking through the woods. And her dress is long and green and silk and it goes—swish—swish—swish—through the hush, hush, hush.

JOE. (*He imitates* MIMI. *He holds his coat tails like a dress.*) Swish—swish—swish—!

STINKER. Hush—hush—hush—! (*He, too, holds his suit coat like a dress.*)

MIMI (*delighted—runs over to them*). Do it again—do it again!

JOE. Swish—hush—hush—swish——

STINKER. Let me do the hush—you do the swish.

JOE. I want to do the hush—you do the swish. (*They begin to wrestle with each other.*)

EDDIE. (*Grabs them by the coat collar.*) Stop—cut it out——

MIMI. Cut it out. But don't stop. (*She turns back to* MRS. LARUE.) And the little squirrels and the little chipmunks hop behind my mother fast, fast, and the lions and the bears walk behind her slow—slow—slow. Then she is gone. Where is she going? (*She asks this question of* MRS. LARUE.)

MRS. LARUE. I wouldn't have the vaguest idea. Why on earth ask me?

EDDIE (*his eyes on* MIMI). Do you suppose there really is a dame like this doing an animal act up in them mountains?

MRS. LARUE. This is all very odd. This child is very odd, and I thought so from the first. She is obviously trash. (*Although* MRS. LARUE *has said this last line in a low tone,* MIMI *heard it. She nods happily.*)

MIMI. Oh, yes, I am trash. That's where my mother found me when I was a dear little baby only three days old. I was in a trash basket in an alley. They threw me out. Trash is very nice. Soft, soft oranges, soft, soft tomatoes, old shoes, old papers. Mrs. McThing took me with her up to the Blue, Blue Mountains and she raised me.

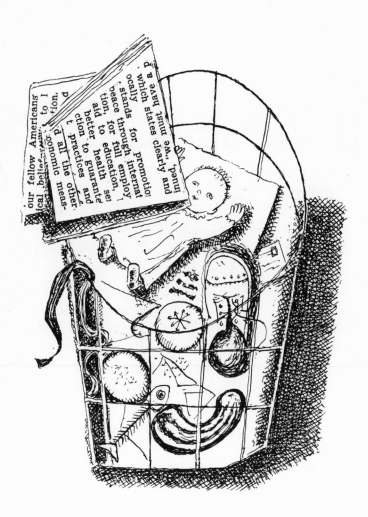

MRS. LARUE. Oh, so you are an adopted child.

MIMI. I am my mother's dear little white rose.

MRS. LARUE. If it's so nice up there, little girl, why don't you stay home? It sounds as if you have things to play with—chipmunks and whatever else it was you mentioned. Why don't you stay up in the beautiful Blue, Blue Mountains with your mother? (*She leaves the room and the door closes behind her.*)

EDDIE (*to* MIMI). She's right, kid. Why don't you go home?

MIMI. I want to play with the boy.

EDDIE. Cut that out. He'll have no time to play with you from now on. He's been promoted. He's gonna be workin' with me and the boys. Now you go home.

MIMI. (*She stamps her foot.*) You can't send me home. My mother is a witch.

EDDIE. What do you think my mother is—a goat?

MIMI. Is your mother a witch, too?

EDDIE. (*He looks around anxiously.*) Shhh—don't you say I ever said that. You hear me? Well, then, if you won't go home—go to work. Take this broom. (*He takes a broom out of the corner and hands it to her.*) Go to work. Nobody loafs around here. Get busy in the kitchen. Go on, get out——
(MIMI *takes the broom and runs into the kitchen.*)

JOE. Boss, if the kid's old lady is really a witch, you'll never see that broom again.

EDDIE. Shut up! Come on in my office. Our meeting is getting cold.
(EDDIE *and the boys go into the boss's office. And at this moment,* MRS. LARUE *returns. She goes over*

*to the table where she had been sitting and she
looks on the chairs and on the floor. The* CHEF *now
raises the wooden shutter on his window and
watches her.*)

CHEF. Lose somethin', lady?

MRS. LARUE. I must have left my bag in here some place.
Oh, here it is! There isn't anything in it but a lipstick,
but I like it.

CHEF. It's real pretty, lady. There is nothing I like better
than a nice brown suede bag. I'm nuts about 'em. I
bought eighteen of 'em for my sister one Christmas.

MRS. LARUE. Oh—well, now where are my gloves? I
dropped them, too. Here they are.

(*She cannot see the door from the lunchroom open
because she has her back turned, but we can see
it open, and in comes* HOWAY. *He is now wearing
a gray derby hat just like* POISON EDDIE'*s, a gray
checked suit, a red shirt and an orange necktie. He
walks with a gangster slouch. He has forgotten
that he was a pampered rich boy. He has made
up his mind to be the toughest member of* EDDIE'*s
mob. He sees the* CHEF—*but he does not see his
mother. He passes the* CHEF'*s window on his way
to the boss's office.*)

HOWAY. Hi-ya, Ellsworth—don't answer!

CHEF. The boss has called a meeting—they're in there.

HOWAY. Ahhhhhhhhhhhhhhhh shaddup!

(MRS. LARUE *has turned at the first sound of the
voice. She stares at him. Now he turns and sees
her and they stare silently for one half second at
each other, both in utter amazement. She walks
slowly toward him. She takes hold of his shoul-*

83

ders and shakes him.)

MRS. LARUE. (*Her voice is full of strange wonder.*) You—here—like this? How dare you? How could you?

HOWAY. You—know—me?

MRS. LARUE. (*Her voice is now a combination of hysteria, passionate indignation and maternal fierceness.*) Know you? Know you? What a question! Why I would know you on the blackest night of the world, in the deepest part of the ocean! Are you simple minded enough to think there was ever anybody like you anywhere in the whole wide world? Know you? Know you? Heavens! (*She stops shaking him now but she still keeps hold of him tightly.*) Oh, aren't you ashamed, what trick have you played on me? Answer me. Answer me.

HOWAY. Let go, Mother. You're pinching me.

MRS. LARUE. I will not let go. (*Suddenly she looks frightened.*) Who—is—HE?

HOWAY. Mrs. McThing got mad at you. She put a Stick in my bed that looked just like me.

MRS. LARUE (*nodding her head*). Even to the birthmark and the scar on the leg. How cruel! But why didn't you come home? What was the matter with you?

HOWAY. I tried—I did try—but I couldn't get in.

MRS. LARUE. Oh, why didn't you try harder? Just think—if I hadn't come here tonight I suppose you would have let me live and die without you. Didn't you ever think of me—your own mother?

HOWAY. I thought you liked him better—that Stick.

MRS. LARUE. He looked like you. Who wouldn't like anybody who looked like you?

84

HOWAY. Oh, he is clean and I wasn't!

MRS. LARUE. Don't be silly.

HOWAY. He studied his lessons all the time.

MRS. LARUE. Oh, stop it—stop it——

HOWAY. And he kissed the Loomis girls——

MRS. LARUE. What of it?

HOWAY. And he didn't make you worry.

MRS. LARUE. He gave me an inferiority complex. How could I have endured it? Howay, didn't you want to see me—didn't you miss me?

HOWAY. Well— (*He looks around cautiously.*)

MRS. LARUE. Didn't you—didn't you?

HOWAY. It makes me sound like a cream puff to say it— you promise you won't tell anybody?

MRS. LARUE. I promise—I promise——

HOWAY. I did, Mother, I missed you. (*He puts his arms around her and they clasp each other.*)

MRS. LARUE. Howay, oh, Howay! Well, come on, let's go home—right away.

HOWAY. I can't. I can't go.

MRS. LARUE. Can't go! What do you mean, you can't go?

HOWAY. Mother—I—I joined the mob. You can't get out of a mob.

MRS. LARUE. You joined a mob! But, darling, that's foolish. (*She laughs.*) You can't join a mob. You're only a baby.

HOWAY. (*This doesn't please him at all.*) Don't say that, Mother. I'm NOT a baby any more. I'm a mobster now. I been able to hold my own with these guys down here. Mr. Schellenbach says I'll go places.

MRS. LARUE. You'll go no place but home. Now that I've found you again I will never let you go. And nobody in the world can take you away from me—never.

HOWAY. I've got to stay here, Mother.

MRS. LARUE. Howay, you're frightening me. You're giving me the feeling I'm losing you again. Come home with me. We've got to be together. You don't expect your mother to stay in a vile place like this, do you? (MIMI *comes into the room from the kitchen door.* MRS. LARUE *sees her and pushes* HOWAY *behind her so as to prevent* MIMI *from seeing him.*) You—you—get away. This all began the day you climbed over our wall.

MIMI. I want to play with your boy. I like him.

MRS. LARUE. (*She stamps her foot as though she were stamping at a mangy cat or a muddy dog.*) Get out— get out!

HOWAY. Mother, don't. She only wants to play with me.

MRS. LARUE. She climbed in our place that day because you have a pony and a white swan-boat. You get away from him and you stay away from him. Get out!

MIMI. (*Her voice is quiet but there is a deadly note in it. She points her forefinger at* MRS. LARUE.) That—was your last chance. You get no more chances. Never—— (*She walks to the door and turns.*) Never, no more. No more chances. (*She goes out and the door slams behind her.*)

HOWAY. Oh, Mother, you shouldn't have done that.

MRS. LARUE. (*If she has been the least bit affected by* MIMI's *strange words she does not show it. She walks proudly to the telephone, holding* HOWAY *by the hand tightly. She drops a dime into the slot and dials.*) I know what I'm doing. I'm going to call the house right away and have them send the car down here for us. I'll build a higher wall around Larue Towers. I'll hire a bodyguard to watch you while you sleep. I'll never let you out of my sight again. They'll never get another stick in our place. Stand close to me here. I don't want you to get an inch away. (*Looks at him closely.*) Oh, that dreadful suit! (*She is waiting for the telephone to answer.* HOWAY *looks crushed. He thinks this is the most beautiful suit he ever owned. It is a genuine gangster suit.* EDDIE *gave it to him. The telephone at the Larue house must have answered by this time.* MRS. LARUE *speaks into the receiver.*) Hello, Nelson? This is Mrs. Larue speaking. No, I don't want to speak to Mrs. Larue. This is Mrs. Larue speaking. (*She turns to* HOWAY.) Nelson must have cotton in his ears. He said he would go and see if Mrs. Larue would speak with me. (*A funny expression crosses* HOWAY's *face. He looks at his mother.*) Hello—this is Mrs. Larue—you're who? Who did you say you were? Don't be silly. *I* am Mrs. Larue. (*She turns to* HOWAY, *who now knows what has happened even if his mother doesn't.*) They're acting crazy out there. You—get off the line—put Carrie on the line. You what! *You* sent her to her sister's for a vacation. *I* sent her to her sisters for a vacation. Who are you? (*She lets the ear piece drop from her hands. It swings back and forth on the cord.* MRS. LARUE, *with staring eyes, places her hand on her cheek, she takes a weak step forward.*) What—what's happened to me? I'm not myself—I——

HOWAY. Don't you see, Mother. Mrs. McThing has

87

skunked you again. She's put a stick in your place now.

MRS. LARUE. (*She gazes at him in terror.*) Howay!— Howay!

   (*The receiver by the telephone is still swinging loosely back and forth as the* CURTAIN *comes down.*)

ACT TWO

SCENE 1

THE SET: *The Shantyland Pool Hall Lunchroom.*

THE TIME: *A few days later.*

The curtain rises and we see the CHEF *playing his piano and a woman in a faded old apron sweeping the floor. This woman looks familiar to us. Haven't we seen her some place before? We look more closely.*

Yes. It is MRS. HOWARD V. LARUE III *but how she has changed! She is no longer wearing the smart silk gown. Now she wears a too large cotton dress, with a rip by the pocket, and an old apron over it. Her hair no longer has those tight neat little curls but hangs limply and one strand falls across her cheek. Where are her small black satin slippers with the high heels? Her feet are in old tennis shoes, tied not with laces but with string.*

She is having trouble with the broom, too. She has never handled a broom before and she is holding it as though it were a live animal. When she sweeps she pushes one little pile of dirt ahead of her as though she were shoveling snow. She looks very discouraged. But suddenly her eyes gleam. She has seen something on the floor. She picks it up. It is a dime. Joyfully she runs to the telephone, slips the dime in the slot and dials a number.

We can tell by her face that she believes something very good will happen to her from finding that dime.

MRS. LARUE. (*Finally her number has answered.*) Evva—
Evva Loomis—this is Belle—Belle Larue—your best
friend. (*She listens. What she is hearing is* EVVA
LOOMIS *telling her she can't possibly be* BELLE LARUE.
BELLE LARUE *is having tea with her this moment.*) But,
Evva, you've known me since I was a girl. You were
one of my bridesmaids. I tell you that woman is not I.
She's a stick—she is a STICK! I am Belle Larue. Oh,
please—please——(*She listens a moment and then slowly
hangs up the receiver and speaks to the* CHEF.) She
hung up on me. (HOWAY *now comes in from the
lunchroom. If his mother looks sad and discouraged
and out of place in Shantyland, her son does not. He
is wearing his gangster suit. He walks like a gangster
and he is happy. He is using his gangster gestures and
speech. He sees his mother and goes—"Hi-ya" just
like* EDDIE. MRS. LARUE'*s face lights up at the sight of
him.*) Darling! I haven't seen you all day.

HOWAY (*very proudly*). I been with the mob.

MRS. LARUE. (*She is examining him closely.*) Howay
Larue! You didn't wash!

HOWAY (*trying to pull away from her*). I did. I did.

MRS. LARUE (*pulling him over to the table where there
is a pitcher of water.*) Look at those ears. You come
here. (*She dips a corner of the apron into the water
and goes after his ears. He struggles. But her hold is
firm. He is in an agony of embarrassment.*) I don't
know why you will insist upon going around like a
dirty pig. Stand still.

HOWAY (*trying to pull away*). The mob is waiting for
me. Let go.

MRS. LARUE (*as she works furiously on his ears*). Other people's children can keep themselves clean.

HOWAY (*his eyes on the boss's door*). Oh, Mother, don't let Mr. Schellenbach see you washing my ears.

CHEF. (*He leans out of his window.*) Do what she tells you, kid.

HOWAY. They're clean now. Let go. (*Now he is able to pull away.*)

CHEF. Kid, when it comes to washing yourself, be guided. Listen to your mother. This is a tough world. You gotta keep your ears clean because some day you're liable to run into somebody who's gonna pin 'em back.

MRS. LARUE. You hear that, Howay? I'm not the only one. Now go and comb your hair.

HOWAY (*as he hurries out of the room*). Oh darn!

MRS. LARUE (*to the* CHEF). What is the matter with that boy? Does he want to grow up a bum? End in skid row? (*She stops and looks around.*) Oh! I forgot where I am. Thank you, Ellsworth, for helping me with him. That was nice of you.

CHEF. He's a pretty good kid, Belle. Of course you'll never believe this, but there was a time when I looked worse than he does. I know that's hard to believe, but it's true. Oh, I know it ain't easy for you, Belle, tryin' to raise your boy and wash dishes and sweep floors, too. But don't you worry about him.

MRS. LARUE. Oh, play for me Ellsworth—make me forget.

CHEF. Sure. (*He unloosens his fingers.*) What'll it be?

MRS. LARUE. I feel like Tchaikovsky's *Fifth.*

CHEF. For that one I gotta look like this—

> (*The* CHEF *makes a horrible face as though he were about to cry. He also bares his teeth as though he were about to bite. Then he goes into the number while* MRS. LARUE *leans against the shelf and looks sad.*
>
> *The door of the boss's office opens and out comes* EDDIE. *He frowns as he sees the broom lying on the floor and the* CHEF *playing.*)

EDDIE. Hey, what's goin' on here?

> (MRS. LARUE *gets a frightened look on her face, picks up the broom and sweeps her way into the kitchen. The* CHEF *quickly leaves his window.* EDDIE *looks mad.* HOWAY *walks in. His hair is now combed.*)

EDDIE. Hey you, squirt, come here.

HOWAY. Yes, Mr. Schellenbach.

EDDIE. When you ran in here chased by that cop and I took you on, little did I dream I'd have to put your whole family on the payroll.

HOWAY. You've been swell, Mr. Schellenbach.

EDDIE. Okay, okay. Is there anybody else up at your place this Mrs. McThing is liable to double up on?

HOWAY. Oh, no! In our family there is just me and my mother.

EDDIE. We all get a break once in a while. You could have had a pop, six brothers and a sister and a cousin twice removed.

HOWAY. But I don't.

EDDIE. Good! Because I don't want to be runnin' a flop house for characters this Mrs. McThing is liable to

93

double cross in the future. Now, we all got mothers. I got one. Joe has got one. Even the Stinker has got one. And you—well maybe you got two—which makes it a lot tougher on you than most of us. Kid, I've got to let you have it straight. This mother of yours is not workin' out around here. (*At this moment we hear off stage in the kitchen the deafening sound of a great pile of dishes crashing to the floor. A bitter look crosses* EDDIE's *face.*) You see what I mean?

HOWAY. Oh—— (*This is a new situation for* HOWAY. *He has a puzzled look on his face. Always before, people complained to his mother about him. Sometimes* CARRIE *complained about him—sometimes his tutor and the gardener or* NELSON. *But here is a man complaining about his mother to him. What is he supposed to do? Since he doesn't know, he sits and says nothing. But* EDDIE *goes on.*)

EDDIE. Her attitude may be O.K. Most of them dishwashers wash dishes and cuss the chef. She don't cuss the chef, but she don't wash dishes either. She breaks 'em. And she can't sweep. Look at them corners. Her work don't satisfy me and I am not what you would call a particularly clean mobster, am I?

HOWAY (*proudly*). Oh no, Mr. Schellenbach!

EDDIE. What's the matter with her? You did a better job in that kitchen than she does. You talk to her. Be firm with her. Bawl her out.

HOWAY. Bawl her out!

EDDIE. And show her how. Tell her if she don't improve and quick I'm gonna have to let her go. (JOE *and* STINKER *run in from the street door very excited. They are breathing rapidly.*)

94

JOE. Hey Boss, wait'll you hear——

STINKER. You'll call a meetin'——

EDDIE. (*He is very interested. What is this big news the boys have brought?*) Okay, I call it. (*He walks rapidly to his office. The boys follow and* HOWAY *also. But at the door* EDDIE *sees* HOWAY *and shakes his head.*) Not you. You do what I told you first and then you can join the meeting. (*They all go in the office and* HOWAY *is left outside of the door.*)

HOWAY. Ellsworth, would you let my mother come out here a minute? I've got to—— Well, I've got to—would you let her come out?

CHEF. Belle, leave the dishes a minute. Your boy wants to see you. (MRS. LARUE *comes out of the kitchen door. She is wiping her hands on her apron. Her hair looks more stringy than ever.*)

HOWAY. (*He is looking at her. How does one begin to bawl one's mother out? Gee! But remember what the boss said.*) Mother—— (*She turns and smiles at him. Somehow he can't say it.*) Would you—like a doughnut?

MRS. LARUE. I would, but I can't have one. Mr. Schellenbach doesn't like for the help to eat those doughnuts.

HOWAY. (*Gets one for her and brings it to her.*) I can get it for you. I'm in the mob.

MRS. LARUE. Oh how I shudder when you say that! Oh, thank you, dear. This one is chocolate covered, too. (*She bites into it.*) Oh, but this is good!

CHEF (*leans his head out the window*). Belle, when you get a few minutes would you mind getting back here in the dish water. There's a stack this high.

HOWAY. Ellsworth never talked that nice to me.

MRS. LARUE. Dear, that's what I've always tried to tell you. Good manners are very important. I've been polite to the man. (*She starts back to the kitchen.*) What was it you wanted to see me about?

HOWAY. Oh—oh—nothing. I just wanted to give you a doughnut.

MRS. LARUE. Oh you lamb! If it wasn't for you—I couldn't carry on here. (*She goes back into the kitchen. EDDIE and the boys now come out of the office. They look full of big news. They are all gazing with great interest at HOWAY.*)

EDDIE. (*Isn't his voice a little sweeter than it ever was before? Why?*) Look, squirt——

HOWAY. I told her, Mr. Schellenbach. Boy, was I ever tough with her! She'll get on the beam now.

EDDIE. Sit down, kid. (HOWAY *sits on one of the boxes near* JOE *and* STINKER.) Oh, no, you sit here—at my table with me.

HOWAY. At your table—gosh, Mr. Schellenbach! I don't get it.

EDDIE. You will, kid. We got news—we're goin' on a job. And you're our key man.

HOWAY. A job—at last! Me—the key man. Oh boy! Where —a bank—a safe—another mob?

EDDIE. Tell him, boys!

JOE. Your house—we're goin' to your house!

HOWAY. (*What a let down!*) Our house?

JOE. Stinker and me were out there today.

STINKER. We looked over the wall——

96

JOE. What a swell lay out!

STINKER. A house as big as the court house!

JOE. A garden bigger than the city park!

STINKER. A swan—this big—floatin' on the lake!

HOWAY. That's my boat.

JOE. And a kid that looks just like you riding a white pony with a black saddle.

STINKER. Say, who is that kid?

HOWAY. That's me.

EDDIE. You—but you're here.

HOWAY. Oh sure.

JOE. He's out there.

HOWAY. Oh yes.

STINKER. Who are you?

HOWAY. I'm him.

STINKER. Boss, this is a new snatch racket.

JOE. A new high in a double cross.

EDDIE. Shut up. I'm not tryin' to figure who is who. I'm only lookin' how I can use it. See here, squirt.

JOE. We go out there and rob the place. You get us on the inside.

HOWAY. I can't get in. Those sticks have got it. It's not our house any more.

STINKER. Who's got it?

HOWAY. Oh, it's our house. I mean it was. But they won't let us in.

EDDIE. Here is the pitch. You come with us. Lookin' so much like that kid, you can get us in—quietly—or else —we take rods and blast through the gates, and you

98

can show us where the silver is hid.

HOWAY. No. I don't want to go.

JOE. Lookit him, Boss—he's yella.

STINKER. He's a cream puff.

HOWAY. (*He is very excited.*) I'm not yellow—I'm not a cream puff. I don't want to go back there. I don't like it there. At night, in my bedroom, I can hear the other kids playin' down the road.

JOE. Aw, who cares? Let 'em play. Aw, slush.

EDDIE. Wait—I know what this kid means. I heard that sound. It is horrifying. It is worse than the clang of cell doors behind you in stir. It is worse than police sirens. Alone in your room after supper, hearin' the gang playin' down at the corner. (EDDIE's *face grows sad and wistful as he remembers. But suddenly he forgets, too. His hand goes into his gun pocket.*) But we go out there and blast anyway. Kid, you don't stay there. You lead us to the stuff and you come back with us. You're in the mob. You don't have to stay home.

HOWAY (*miserably*). When I get home I always have to stay. That's the way it always is. I know it. (*He pounds his fist on the table.*) I won't go. I won't go.

EDDIE. (*He is now very angry with* HOWAY.) I tell you you'll come back so don't you tell me you won't go. Listen you—this is our big chance and you're workin' with us. Why, you little creep, I got a good mind——
   (*He reaches out to seize* HOWAY *but just at that moment* MRS. SCHELLENBACH *appears in the doorway.* EDDIE *sees her and lets out a loud cry, "Mama," and runs into his office. Terrified,* JOE *and* STINKER *run into the street and* HOWAY *runs into the kitchen at breakneck speed. She follows her son across the stage and goes into his office after him. Then we*

hear the sound of cuffing and slapping. We hear
EDDIE *crying out, "Don't hit me again, Mama. I*
didn't do nothin'." Then the door of the office
opens and MRS. SCHELLENBACH *comes out, rubbing*
her palms together. Without a word she crosses
the stage and goes out.

> MRS. LARUE *and the* CHEF *have appeared at the*
> CHEF's *window in time to see her leave. They*
> *watch as she walks across the room in short hard*
> *steps.*)

MRS. LARUE (*shaking her head*). Poor old soul! She has got a problem. Hers is worse than mine. Her boy's habit pattern is pretty well set. There is always somebody worse off than we are. I feel better about my own son when I see hers.

> (*The lights now go out in the lunchroom and we see*
> *again the street outside. The three Loomis girls*
> *are coming down the street. They stand before*
> *the door to the lunchroom.*)

EVVA. Yes, she said Shantyland Pool Hall Lunchroom. My, what a dirty old place! (EVVA *is suddenly afraid to go inside. But of course she doesn't want her sisters to know she is afraid of anything. She has told them so many times that nothing ever scared her. So she turns now and puts her hand gently on* MAUDE's *shoulder.*) I think it would be wiser, dear, if we didn't all go in at once. You go in first, Maude dear, and look around. We'll wait for you here.

MAUDE. (*She is frightened, too.*) But, Evva, you always go first.

EVVA (*firmly*). It's time you were getting some initiative of your own. Stand on your own feet for a change. Go

100

inside. Grace will be right behind you. Go on. (*She pushes her.*)

> (*The light on the street is now darkened and lights now come on again inside the lunchroom. The room is empty.*
>
> *We see poor old* MAUDE *through the door. She looks around, tries to run out—but she is pushed from behind. She comes in then a step at a time. She looks at the old packing boxes, at the boss's office, at the* CHEF's *window and the dust on the floor. She shivers. This place is not only grim—it is deserted. Perhaps there is no one here at all.* GRACE *now comes cautiously inside and behind her,* EVVA.)

EVVA (*in a whisper*). It looks deserted. Maybe this isn't the place after all. But she did say the back of the Shantyland Pool Hall Lunchroom.

MAUDE. I don't like it. Let's go. (*They are all starting to leave, but they stop at the door.* MRS. LARUE *has come out of the kitchen. She has gone over to the packing boxes and is placing them in a neater stack against the wall. She does not see the Loomis girls.* MAUDE *gets close to* EVVA.) Look!

EVVA. Shhh—— (*She curls her forefinger for her sisters to keep quiet. They will get out of there. But* MRS. LARUE *has looked up. She sees them. Her face lights up with happiness. She drops her broom.*)

MRS. LARUE. Girls! You came! Come on in—come in! Oh, you did come! You didn't forget me after all. Oh, my dear, dear friends—bless you—bless you. (*She runs to them to throw her arms around them.*)

EVVA (*backing away. Her face is cold.*) Who are you?

101

MRS. LARUE. Evva! Evva! You know who I am! I am Belle—Isabelle Larue—your dearest friend.

MAUDE. Sister, is it—or isn't it?

GRACE. But it couldn't be!

EVVA. It's a cunning scheme of some kind. I admit you do look like our best friend, Belle Larue—but who are you?

MRS. LARUE. Oh girls, I told you about Mrs. McThing.

EVVA. *You* told us about Mrs. McThing? Belle Larue told us about Mrs. McThing.

MRS. LARUE. Oh girls, look at me! We all grew up together. We were children together. We were all through school together. You had the place next to ours.

EVVA. Everybody would know where our place was.

MRS. LARUE. Oh, Evva! Remember that time we were in Europe and Maude lost the passports in Paris and you slapped her.

EVVA. I never slapped my sister in my life.

MAUDE (*runs to her and pulls her sleeve*). Yes, you did, Evva, you did. She's right. Whoever she is—she's right.

EVVA (*giving her sister a fierce look*). I did not—but I will——

GRACE. Oh Evva, look at her. (*She points to* MRS. LARUE.) I'm scared!

EVVA. We only left Belle Larue five minutes ago. She had a manicure and a new permanent wave. And you— look at you!

MRS. LARUE. Girls—Mrs. McThing—she made a stick which looks just like me and put her in Larue Towers. I am Belle Larue. Oh, look at me closely—ask me anything. I am the real Belle Larue. Take me out of here—

102

take me with you——

GRACE. Evva, what shall we do?

(EVVA *stands thinking. There is something very odd
about all of this. She is thinking that Mrs. Mc-
Thing must be a most unusual person. Because
whichever one is the stick the witch made—they
look exactly alike. Suppose the woman at Larue
Towers is the stick? Or, suppose this dirty scrub-
woman is the stick? One of them is the stick.
But, says* EVVA *to herself, the one out at Larue
Towers can serve them tea and cake and give
them roses and take them for drives in her beautiful shiny black limousine. So now* EVVA *knows
which is which.*)

EVVA (*slowly*). Yes, girls—it is apparent that Mrs. Mc-
Thing made a stick which looks just like Belle Larue——

MRS. LARUE (*hopeful*). Of course, she did, she did!

EVVA. Why she did, I don't know and that is her business
and not mine—but she did. And—it is quite apparent
that you are that stick. Come, girls, let us go. And you
stop bothering us on the telephone——

MR. LARUE (*running after them. She grabs* EVVA's *arm*).
Evva, Maude, Grace—you're not going to leave me
here.

EVVA. Take your hands off me, you stick!

MRS. LARUE. Me—a stick! Why you—you come down here
and insult me and you're wearing a dicky off my living-
room chair. (*She runs to* MAUDE *and snatches off the
lace piece which* MAUDE *has pinned at her neck.*) Give
me back my antimacassar.

(MAUDE *screams.* MRS. LARUE *picks up her broom.
The girls are running out of the door. She stands*

103

in the doorway and calls after them.)

MRS. LARUE. If I ever get home you'll run faster than that. (*We can hear them screaming and sputtering as they run up the street.* MRS. LARUE *turns away from the door. The broom slips from her hand. Her temper has now given way to sadness and despair. The Loomis girls were her only hope. Now they have let her down. She is doomed to stay in this place forever. She sinks into a chair by one of the tables and lays her head down on her arms. Then she hears someone coming. She picks her head up and wipes her eyes. It is* HOWAY.)

HOWAY. Mother, what's the matter?

MRS. LARUE. (*She manages to smile at him.*) Nothing— nothing at all, dear. I'm fine—just fine.

HOWAY. That's good! You like it here, don't you, Mother? Gee, so do I. That's why I told Mr. Schellenbach I wouldn't go home.

MRS. LARUE. Home! Home! What did you say, Howay?

HOWAY. (*He has not noticed her eager expression.*) Mr. Schellenbach and the mob wanted to go out there tonight.

MRS. LARUE. Out there—at Larue Towers. Those sticks are there. Nobody can get in.

HOWAY. He said he was gonna blast with rods—and get through that gate.

MRS. LARUE. (*This is a new thought.*) Guns—I wonder. Oh what I wouldn't give to be able to go home, especially right now! Howay—Howay—— (*Her eyes are beginning to sparkle.*) I wonder if it would work?

Guns—I never thought of that. But maybe it would work—yes—maybe it would! Oh, Howay—darling—darling—— Just suppose it did? We could try it anyway. (*She gets up from the chair she has been sitting in and runs quickly across the rooms and knocks on the boss's door.*) Mr. Schellenbach, Mr. Schellenbach. (*The door opens and* EDDIE *stands there.*) Oh, Mr. Schellenbach, you have a wonderful idea. We'll go with you—let's try it. Howay and I will change our clothes—right now. It's wonderful—it's wonderful——

EDDIE. You're a sensible woman, Belle. I better start lookin' around for my artillery—— (*He closes door.*)

MRS. LARUE. Yes—yes——Come, Howay, don't stand there —you've got to get your clothes changed. Oh, how I hate that hat! (*She takes the gray derby off his head and throws it into a corner.*)

HOWAY. (*He rescues the hat and jams it back on his head. His face has a stubborn expression.*) I like it here, Mother. I got friends here. Why do we have to go home?

MRS. LARUE. Friends, yes, but not your type, dear. Good people, of course, but not quite right for you. (*She walks to his side.*) There is nobody like you, Howay, and that's not just because you're my child. I know. I've observed other children and they don't have that certain something you have. You are very, very special. (*But he pulls away from her sullenly. This makes no impression on him. She is now worried. She smiles brightly and changes her tactics.*) Darling, just listen to this. I'll buy you an Alaskan husky dog right away. We'll get that chemical company to freeze the lake and you can go dog sledding even in summer.

HOWAY. Could—could Mr. Schellenbach and the mob come home with us?

MRS. LARUE. (*This makes her lose her patience.*) Those people at home with us? Oh, Howay! You are incorrigible. I'm losing my patience with you. Don't you care anything about me? Do you like to see your mother washing dishes? I want to be in my own home—my own bed—wake up to look out on my own garden. I've been so unhappy. Doesn't that mean anything to you? Don't you love me at all?

HOWAY. (*He sighs. She has beaten him. He can hold out no longer. He would like to be able to tell her that terrible feeling he has at home at night in his bedroom when he hears the other kids playing down the road. But he cannot tell her. So often it is impossible to tell the right things to the people who should hear them. So he sighs deeply.*) Okay!

MRS. LARUE. (*She is happy instantly. She begins to run—calling back to him.*) Get your own clothes—get ready. Let's hurry—hurry—I can't get away from here fast enough. (*She runs out.*)

(HOWAY *looks around. He cannot understand what she means. She can't get away from here fast enough? This is a beautiful place. And it smells good, too—the chef always cooking hamburgers and hot dogs, the old brick walls, the boss's door with the boss's name, the music from the chef's piano—oh, everything!*

He sits down on one of the packing boxes. He has decided he'd better take a good look at it. He may never see it again.

We will leave HOWAY *sitting sadly on the box while*

106

*we go outside into the street and see what is hap-
pening. We see* JOE *and* STINKER *sitting on the
curbing.* MIMI *now comes skipping happily up the
street. She is skipping past them when* JOE *reaches
out and grabs her.*)

JOE. Hey, where you goin'?

MIMI. I'm going to play with the boy.

JOE. He can't play with you now.

STINKER. He's goin' on a job with us—leave him alone.

JOE. You can play with us if you wanta play.

STINKER (*to* JOE). But what if she wants to play fair?

MIMI. I came down from the Blue, Blue Mountains to
play with the boy.

JOE. Oh, you and your fairy stories.

MIMI. I will tell you a story—a sad, sad story, and you've
got to cry. Some day my mother will take me to the
edge of the woods and she will kiss me good-bye. Because I am people and some day I must go to live with
people. It will break her heart to say good-bye but she
must do it and it will break my heart to hear her—but
I must do it. Because your heart has to break—and
yours and yours——(*She is pointing to* JOE *and*
STINKER.) and everybody's heart has to break—— Now
cry!

JOE. (*He is crying hard and wiping his eyes.*) Gee, kid!

MIMI. Everybody's got to cry. (*She points her finger
sternly at* STINKER.) He's not crying.

STINKER. Okay—so I'll cry.

JOE. Cry then and don't just sit there sayin' you're gonna
cry. Cry!

107

STINKER. I'm not gonna just sit here sayin' I'm gonna cry. I'm gonna cry. Booo—hooooo!

MIMI. Now stop! That's enough crying—you must never cry too long.

JOE. When did this happen, kid?

MIMI. Not yet—my mother says not yet—too young yet. Wait a while!

JOE. (*He jumps up. He is insulted.*) You mean we been bawlin' about somethin' that ain't even happened yet? (*To* STINKER.) Stop bawling. It ain't even happened yet. (*Now* JOE *looks up and sees* HOWAY *coming out of the door of Shantyland, his hands in his pockets. He is walking up the street away from them. Where is he going?* JOE *would like to know this, too. He runs into the lunchroom.*) Boss—hey, boss. The kid's takin' a run-out. Boss—boss!

    (*The* STINKER *follows him on the run.* MIMI, *who is left on the street alone, starts to run after* HOWAY.)

MIMI. Howay—Howay!

    (HOWAY *sees her and turns around. He comes slowly to where she is. His hands are in his pants pockets. He sits down on the curbing.*)

HOWAY. Mimi, we're going home. We're going back. My mother says so.

MIMI. My mother says no.

HOWAY. But Mr. Schellenbach is going to take rods and blast.

MIMI. Ha—ha—ha—guns won't get rid of sticks.

HOWAY. (*He jumps up.*) They won't—then maybe I *can* stay here. (*Then he remembers something and he slowly sinks to the curbing again.*) No. My mother is

109

so unhappy. We have to go, but I'll come back some day and be in the mob again. Mimi, if guns won't get rid of sticks, what does? Can you find how in a book?

MIMI. Oh no!

HOWAY. Do you hold your left ear and spit three times in a creek?

MIMI. Oh no!

HOWAY. I wonder how.

MIMI. I know. My mother knows and I know.

HOWAY. You know, Mimi? (*She nods.*) Will you do it?

MIMI. If I do, will your mother let you play with me?

HOWAY. Yes. She'll have to. I'll make her. Do you really know how, Mimi?

MIMI. My mother knows and I know. Mimi, you hear too much. (*Now she is imitating her mother's voice and holding her skirts out.*) Sticks are my business. You keep out of my sticks. Oh yes, I know—I know.

HOWAY. Will you get in trouble with your mother if you do it?

MIMI. Yes.

HOWAY. Will you do it anyway?

MIMI. (*She looks at him and nods her head slowly.*) Yes.
    (*Now* MRS. LARUE *comes out into the street from the lunchroom. She is dressed in her silk dress— the one she was wearing the first night she came to look for* HOWAY. *She is also wearing her hat with the little feathers and carrying her brown suede bag and beige gloves.*)

MRS. LARUE. Howay—Howay—what are you doing? Why aren't you getting out of those awful clothes? We're ready to leave.

HOWAY. Mother, Mimi says—she says——

MRS. LARUE (*taking hold of him and pulling him along with her into the lunchroom*). I can't stop for what she says. Say good-bye to her and come along.

HOWAY. (*He pulls back. Oh, why won't she listen!*) But Mother, Mimi says——

MRS. LARUE. Honey, I'm losing my patience. We must not keep Mr. Schellenbach waiting. He's getting everything ready. Little girl—— (*She speaks to* MIMI *who is standing watching, her hands behind her back.*) Howay is busy now. You'd better run along. (*She takes* HOWAY *with her through the door.*)

    (*The lights go out on the street and go up in the lunchroom. We see* MRS. LARUE *pulling* HOWAY *along with her toward the boss's office.* MIMI *is running along behind them. Just before* MRS. LARUE *goes into the office she turns and speaks to* MIMI.)

MRS. LARUE. Little girl, I told you to run along. So run along. (*She takes* HOWAY *in the office with her and* MIMI *is left looking up at the door.*)

    (*And now from someplace there comes a loud knocking—steady, short, sharp knocks. At this sound* MIMI *looks frightened and she runs and hides under the table. The* CHEF *leans out of his window and says, "Come in—come in!" But nobody comes in. We hear the knocking again.*)

MIMI (*to* CHEF). Shhh, it's my mother. Don't tell her I'm here.

CHEF. Your mother—where is she—outside the door there?

MIMI. Shhh—maybe!

CHEF. Well, if your mother wants you, why don't you go?

MIMI. Maybe your mother wants you, too.

CHEF. My mother lives in Wisconsin with my sister Irma and her six kids. Say, what's the matter with your own home? Don't you like it?

MIMI. I like it. Oh yes, but I want to play with the boy.

Do you know what we do at home?

CHEF. No.

MIMI. At night my mother takes my hand and we go down to watch the beaver chewing the logs. Did you know my mother is a good beaver watcher?

CHEF. No.

MIMI. We crawl out far on a low branch over the lake, and we stir up the stars in the water. Did you know my mother was a good star stirrer?

CHEF. No.

MIMI. Don't you know anything?

CHEF. I know how to play this piano.

(*He puts his hands down on the shelf to play and as his fingers barely touch the wood there is the sound of a sudden burst of music from somewhere, as though lightning had struck. Now this music does not sound like the tinkling music box we heard before when* MIMI *spoke of* MRS. MC-THING. *That music said, "Be happy." It was small and pretty. But this music sounds as though someone was up in the Blue, Blue Mountains drawing a bow ten feet long across a violin twenty feet wide. This music says, "Watch out." It stops as suddenly as it came. But the* CHEF *has grown pale and* MIMI *has cowered down deeper under the table.*)

CHEF. What's that? (*His voice is a whisper.*)

MIMI. Shhh, my mother——

(*And now from the boss's office runs* MRS. LARUE *followed by* HOWAY, EDDIE, JOE *and the* STINKER.)

MRS. LARUE. That music—what is it? I'm suddenly frightened.

113

CHEF. Shh—the kid says it's her mother.

MRS. LARUE. Her mother! Mrs. McThing? Oh dear. (*She reaches out and pulls* HOWAY *to her.*) Oh, Mr. Schellenbach, maybe we hadn't better try it. I'm afraid it's no use. There is no way back.

HOWAY. (*He sees* MIMI *under the table.*) Look, Mother! Mimi can do it. She can get you back home.

MIMI. (*She comes out from under the table. Her voice is proud. She tosses her head.*) Oh yes. I can do it. Guns won't do it.

EDDIE. Guns can do anything.

MRS. LARUE. (*She looks at* EDDIE.) I wonder. I wonder. (*She turns to* MIMI.) Little girl, do you know how to do this? You must not say you know if you don't.

HOWAY. She can do it, Mother. She can. She heard her mother talking and she knows how.

EDDIE. You mean this kid knows something I don't know. I doubt it. Kid, once and for all—who are you?

MIMI. I am a dear little white rose.

EDDIE. You could be a whole garden and still know nothing.

MRS. LARUE. Mimi, tell me, have you ever done anything like this before?

MIMI. No.

EDDIE. You mean you got no references for this kind of work?

MRS. LARUE. Mimi, come here. (MIMI *walks to her slowly, her hands behind her back.*) If you've never done this before, why are you willing to do it now?

MIMI. (*She drops her head. She runs the toe of her shoe*

114

around on the floor, drawing circles. When she speaks, it is in such a low tone we can hardly hear her.) Because—I want to go with Howay!

MRS. LARUE (*after a pause*). Mr. Schellenbach, I'm actually afraid to go unless we take her. Very well, Mimi, you lead and we'll follow.

MIMI. Shhh! (*She puts her finger at her lips.*) Don't be afraid—follow me——

(*She walks on tiptoes, motions to them to follow and with everybody walking on tiptoes they follow her,* MRS. LARUE *right behind her, then* HOWAY, *then* EDDIE, *then* JOE *and last of all the* STINKER.

And now they have gone. The door closes behind them.

But no sooner has the door closed when again, suddenly, comes the crash of that warning music— that watch-out music—that music which means MRS. MC THING! MRS. MC THING!

The CURTAIN *comes down on Scene 1 of Act Two.*)

ACT TWO

SCENE 2

THE TIME: *A half hour after the curtain of the previous scene.*

THE SET: *The morning room of Larue Towers again.*

The STICK BOY *in his neat clothes is seated in the center of the satin sofa. He is reading aloud to the Loomis girls and the* STICK MOTHER, *all of whom are seated on little gold chairs.*

The STICK MOTHER *is wearing a handsome silk dress, her hair is neatly curled and her hands are folded stiffly in her lap. The Loomis girls are wearing the same clothes they wore when we saw them last—lacy, ruffled and beaded.*

They are all listening intently to what the STICK *is reading—except* MAUDE. *As usual her eyes are fastened on the candy in the gold dish on the little gold table. It seems* MAUDE *can never listen to anything when there is candy in the room.*

STICK BOY. (*His voice is very prim and proper. His enunciation is perfect. He is sitting straight, head up, shoulders back, chest out. He is reading from a psychology book. He is fond of this type of book. Story books bore him.*) Therefore the problem facing each and every one of us is how to express——

MAUDE (*in a loud whisper*). Pass the candy!

STICK BOY. (*He raises his eyes and frowns at her.*) Shh, please! Please! (*She drops her eyes and then goes on.*)

116

—is how to express each and every facet of his personality——

EVVA. (*She has suddenly remembered something. She smiles and turns to the* STICK MOTHER.) That reminds me, I saw Henrietta Slosson downtown today and she said——

STICK BOY. Shh, Miss Evva, please! (*He frowns at her. She too drops her eyes.*)—express each facet of his personality and be completely comfortable at the same time.

EVVA (*to* STICK MOTHER). I only broke in like that because I really did see Henrietta Slosson today.
  (*The* STICK BOY *is now quite disgusted with them. He slams the book shut. Oh, well, he will read it by himself tonight before he goes to sleep.*)

STICK MOTHER. (*Her voice is stern.*) Of course, dear. You are impulsive. But Howay was absolutely right when he frowned at you for interrupting him.

STICK BOY. Thank you, Mother.

STICK MOTHER. Don't mention it, dear. But perhaps if he doesn't mind we can chat for a few minutes now and then he can begin the next chapter. Is that all right, dear?
  (*The* STICK BOY *nods.*)

MAUDE. Now may I have some candy, Howay?

STICK BOY. Yes, Miss Maude, you may. But you forgot to say please.
  (*There is a terrific noise and clatter outside. The door at the top of the stairs is flung open and* NELSON *comes running down, his heavy boots hitting the steps, clack, clack, clack.*)

NELSON. (*He is breathing rapidly. He has been running*

117

all the way.) Ma'am—ma'am—the lodge keeper at the gate says a gang of hoodlums have just climbed over the wall.

STICK MOTHER. (*Her eyes glitter. She rises and stands stiff as a telegraph pole.*) Call the police, right away.

NELSON. Yes, ma'am—yes, ma'am—— (*He runs back up the stairs.*)

(SYBIL *now runs in from the music room. She is so excited the words jump out of her mouth like corn popping in a hot pan.*)

SYBIL. They're here—up there—I'm scared! Burglars! Down—up—all over.

STICK MOTHER. Sound the alarm—— (*She moves her arm up and down. She looks like a wooden doll which has been wound up.*)

(*The Loomis girls begin to run around the room and the* STICK BOY *tries to hide behind them. But they will not stand still and so he has to keep moving in order to keep hiding.*)

MAUDE (*as she runs*). I want to go home.

STICK BOY. Hide me! Hide me!

EVVA. Maude—Grace—where are you?

STICK MOTHER. Up the stairs.

(*They all rush pell mell to the stairs and start up, when suddenly they stop—the door is slowly opening. Terrified, they back away. The Loomis girls run out through the door to the terrace and the* STICK MOTHER *and* STICK BOY *run and sit stiffly next to each other on the sofa.*

The door at the top of the stairs has now opened and we see EDDIE, *cautiously coming down, fol-*

lowed by the STINKER *and* JOE. *They are carrying sacks. They do not see the two* STICKS. *They stop on the stairs and look around.*)

JOE. (*He is amazed at this beautiful room. Never in his wildest dreams has he been able to imagine such a place.*) What a layout!

EDDIE (*nodding*). A swell roost.

STINKER. (*He is so impressed.*) It's like—it's like the lobby of the Bijou Movie Theater. (*He now sees the* STICKS.) Hey, Boss—look!

EDDIE. (*He looks too. He puts his hand into his gun pocket.*) REACH!
> (*But the* STICKS *make no move at all. They sit like wood. It does not seem that they are breathing. Their eyelids are still as still!*
>
> *The gangsters in single file tiptoe to the sofa and get behind the* STICKS. *Each has his hand in his gun pocket.*)

EDDIE. I said—reach!

JOE. Stick 'em up!

STINKER. (*He is looking at them closely.*) Movie theater—it's a funeral parlor!

EDDIE. (*He stands in front of them now.*) Get movin'—get goin'—come on—come on—— (*He takes hold of the* STICK BOY's *head and turns it around as he would move the head of a department store dummy.*) Look! They ain't breathin', they're stiffs!

JOE. They're stallin'.

EDDIE (*now in a very loud voice*). MOVE!
> (*The gangsters all jump with fear. Outside we hear the sound of police sirens and whistles.*)

JOE (*runs to the terrace window*). Boss, the cops—we're cooked!
> (*EDDIE and JOE run and look out the window, too. Yes, there is no doubt of it. Outside they see ten police cars loaded with police.*)

EDDIE. Run for it, boys, run for it!

120

JOE. Run for it—we're surrounded!

STINKER. Where's Belle? Where's Howay?

EDDIE. They went to the basement to cut the wires.

JOE. They didn't do it in time.
(*The sound of the police sirens is louder and closer.*)

EDDIE. The roof—the roof—we'll make for the roof. (*They dash to the stairs and start up when the door at the top opens slowly and they see* MIMI *entering. She is not the least bit excited nor is she in any hurry. The gangsters stop.*)

JOE. Boss, that kid—she said guns wouldn't do it. Remember!

EDDIE. Yeah, she did say that? Kid! (*He runs to her, his hands are folded pleadingly.*) Whatever you do, do it now.

JOE. And fast. Hear them sirens.

MIMI (*very calmly*). I am a dear little white rose.

EDDIE.(*Oh, why won't she hurry?*) You're a dream—a babe. Hurry up or I'll slug you!
(*But* MIMI *is not to be hurried. She walks slowly down the stairs as the gangsters watch her, the toes of her high buttoned shoes making thump, thumping sounds as she comes down. She has something behind her back but we cannot see what it is. She walks over to the two* STICKS *and she stands before them.*)

MIMI. (*Her voice is like a chant.*)
Knives and stones won't cut your bones,
And guns will never hurt you.
So—burn—sticks—burn!

121

(*And now we see that it is a round red ball she holds behind her back—something like a fire-cracker. She throws it on the ground and there is a big explosion—a burst of red fire—then everything is black. The stage is pitch dark.*

We hear the sound of many feet running and voices calling. Then we see flashlights at the top of the stairs. And we hear NELSON's *voice as he plays the flashlight over the room.*)

NELSON. In here, officers, in here!

(*Two* POLICEMEN *now enter with flashlights. They*

*run down the stairs and by their flashlights we
see bits of the wall, the chairs, the window. Then
the flashlights stop on the three gangsters flattened against the wall.)*

POLICEMAN. Ah—there they are! What pretty pigeons!

NELSON. (*He plays his flashlight upon them, too. They
all look very sheepish.*) Well, if it isn't Poison Eddie
Schellenbach and his boys!

POLICEMAN. Okay, okay, hands up—hands up.

NELSON. Be careful, they'll plug you. They're dangerous.
Let me find a light here.

(NELSON *finds the light and turns it on. The light
floods the whole room. And where the* STICKS *were
sitting we now see two pieces of wood—blackened
and charred—standing upright against the sofa.*
MIMI *is standing between them, looking at them
curiously. The* POLICEMAN *and* NELSON *have not
yet noticed these burned sticks.* MIMI *says nothing.*)

NELSON (*to the gangsters*). Drop your rods on the floor
and raise your hands.

POLICEMAN. I didn't hear nothin' drop. Drop those rods.

SECOND POLICEMAN. (*He runs over and begins to go
through their pockets. Their hands are up. He draws
back and scratches his head.*) These guys ain't got no
guns!

(*No guns! How astonishing! And yet we have seen
them always putting their right hands into their
coat pockets as though each one carried a big rod.
The* POLICEMAN *is still searching them—their
trouser pockets, too.*)

123

You are certainly a tough bunch of yeggs! Look what I found on 'em. (*He holds up what he found.*) Two Superman Comic books! Six Wheatena Box tops! Four packages of bubble gum! You guys are not yeggs—you are cream puffs!

    (EDDIE, JOE *and* STINKER *all hang their heads in shame.*)

NELSON. Wait, I smell smoke. See there! (*He goes over and looks at the burned sticks. He holds them up in his hands.*) Look at these!

POLICEMAN. (*He seizes* EDDIE *again.*) Burnt sticks. Tryin' to set fire to the place, were you?

JOE. I never seen them sticks before in my life.

EDDIE. You can't pin that on us.

STINKER. I never play with matches. You can ask my mother.

MIMI (*very proudly*). I did it. That's the big stick. (*She points.*) And that's the little stick.

    (*But* NELSON *pays no attention to what she says. He has not heard it.*)

NELSON. Let's get handcuffs on these fellows, officers. Tryin' to burn a house down——

POLICEMAN. That's arson. That means a long stretch in the jail house.

EDDIE. We burned nothin'—we—

POLICEMAN. Shut up and hold out your wrists for the bracelets.

    (EDDIE *is about to say something else when suddenly his eyes light up with hope. He looks up. At the top of the stairs stands a friend,* HOWAY!)

HOWAY. Nelson!

124

(NELSON *turns. He sees* HOWAY *and* MRS. LARUE.)

MRS. LARUE. (*She speaks as she walks down the stairs quickly.*) Nelson, what is the meaning of this?

NELSON. I called the cops like you said, ma'am. I found these three bums and them two burned sticks. These bums were trying to set fire to the place.

MRS. LARUE. Take those handcuffs off those men. They are my guests.

HOWAY. They're my mob.

NELSON. Mrs.—ma'am——

MRS. LARUE. Send all the police away. They're trampling my tulips in the garden.

(*The* POLICEMEN *exchange puzzled glances.* NELSON *shrugs his shoulders. He can't figure this! He was told to call the police. He called the police. They came. They caught gangsters and put handcuffs on them. Now* MRS. LARUE *says they are her guests!*

Sullenly, NELSON *and the* POLICE *unlock the handcuffs.* EDDIE, JOE *and* STINKER *are grinning at them.*)

STINKER (*as they unlock his handcuffs*). —and gimme back my bubble gum. It doesn't belong to me. I only borrowed it.

JOE. And my Wheatena box tops.

EDDIE. I'll take my picture of Hopalong. It's autographed.

(*Disgusted, the officers toss these items at them and leave the room with* NELSON. *When they get outside they will use a lot of words to describe the strange actions of women who allow gangsters to stay and be company.*

125

Meantime MRS. LARUE *has walked slowly over to the burned sticks. She is looking at them now. But somehow she cannot bear to touch them. They frighten her. Just think—only a few moments ago these sticks stood between her and her home— her son and his home. Because of them she has had to sweep floors at Shantyland. She shudders. Then looks around the room.*)

MRS. LARUE. Home, home. I could kiss every piece of furniture in this room and every person. (*And who was it brought her home?* MIMI. *There she stands quietly by the sofa.* MRS. LARUE's *eyes now have a tender light as she regards* MIMI. *She goes to her.*) And you—especially you. Oh, you wonderful little girl! You adorable darling! You are a jewel.

MIMI. I am a dear little white rose.

MRS. LARUE. You are that, too. You are everything sweet. (*She turns and sees the gangsters.*) And Mr. Schellenbach, I will never forget how kind you were to me when I was out in the cold, cold world. How you took me in and were so dear to me and would have kept me forever. There isn't anything I wouldn't do for you. Here—— (*She holds up the gold dish.*) Do have some candy!

 (EDDIE *hurries over to her, followed by the* STINKER *and* JOE. *They dive into the dish of chocolates like swimmers on an August afternoon. Each takes a handful and fills his pockets, except the* STINKER. *He takes two handfuls, drops one handful of chocolates into his vest pocket. Then takes off his hat, drops another handful inside the hat and puts it back on his head.*
 MRS. LARUE *only smiles. But the three Loomis sisters,*

*who now stand at the doorway to the terrace,
watch this with disgust. Who are these men? And
why is Belle permitting them to be in her morning room? They look like burglars.*

Then EVVA *looks at Belle Larue. Is this the woman
they were sitting with in this very room a few
moments ago? It looks exactly like her but there
is a difference. She isn't wearing the same dress—
but it is not that. It is another kind of difference.
This woman is smiling. The Belle Larue they
were sitting with while they listened to her son
read, never smiled. This one—this one looks
exactly like the woman they saw at the Shantyland Pool Hall this morning. What to do about
this? Well, decides* EVVA, *she must stick to her
guns. Whatever woman is mistress of Larue
Towers is the one she will call Belle Larue.*

*And that means that she will never indicate that
she has noticed any change. She smiles brightly
at her sisters and motions them to follow her into
the room.)*

EDDIE. This is good candy, Belle—but if you really want
to do something for me, I could use a few bucks, too.

MRS. LARUE (*who has not seen the Loomis girls.*) Anything you want. Just name the figure. I'll write you a
check.

EDDIE. I've been havin' a little trouble with checks lately.
What about the silverware?

MRS. LARUE. Take it, all of it, it's yours!
(*The gangsters run around the room like mice, grab-
ing silver and throwing it into their sacks. But
the Loomis girls are horrified! Giving these men
her silver! Has Belle lost her mind?*)

EVVA. Belle—Belle!

MRS. LARUE. Yes—— (*Then she turns and sees them. She looks at them silently a half second.*) Oh, I beg your pardon. I thought at first you were someone I knew.

GRACE. Someone you knew—why, Belle!

MRS. LARUE (*shakes her head*). It's really amazing how much you look like them. Yes, I see Mrs. McThing has been busy again.

EVVA. (*She starts toward her.*) Mrs. McThing. We've never met her. Oh, Belle!

MRS. LARUE. But I would know my best friends, the Loomis girls, anywhere. Even Mrs. McThing could not fool me. The real Loomis girls are very fond of me. If I were in trouble in the dirtiest corner of the world they would help me. They would never forget the happy times we had as children. And they would know that even though I live in a great house the one thing I can never buy with money is the love of a friend. But I am boring you and I am sure you have an appointment, ladies.

> (EVVA *has grown pale. So have her sisters. They look wistfully around the lovely room and they look out of the window at the lovely gardens— the trees big and inky under the stars. They hear the splashing of the fountains. They remember the fine times they have had here—the cakes, the parties, the laughter and the gifts!*
> *But no more. Belle is sending them home. Each Loomis girl knows, however, that she deserves this. They refused to help Belle when they saw her in Shantyland this morning—even to admit they did recognize her. And in trying to keep*

129

Larue Towers—they have lost it and their friend, too. Sadly they move toward the door and up the staircase. MRS. LARUE *watches them until they get to the top of the stairs.*)

MRS. LARUE. Ladies! (*They turn. Maybe she has changed her mind.*) If you should ever happen to find my friends, the real Loomis girls——

EVVA. Yes, yes——

MRS. LARUE. My real friends who love me—not as the rich Mrs. Larue but as Belle Higgins, their old play-mate——

MAUDE. Go on.

MRS. LARUE. Tell them I will be waiting for them and will love them again.

EVVA. (*She thinks this over a second. When she speaks it is with a low, sad voice.*) Where—can we find them?

MRS. LARUE. Perhaps, some day, you will find them in your own mirror. When you have been lonely enough for long enough. Good night!

(*The Loomis girls go out.*)

EDDIE. (*He approaches* MRS. LARUE *with a full sack, clanking with silver.*) We got everything we could see, Belle. If we missed any pieces, you telephone and we'll come back or you could send them down special delivery. But be sure to insure it. You don't want it to get lost. This is your family silver. It was swell to meet you, Belle.

JOE. Even if you can't sweep.

STINKER. *If* she can't sweep. She *can't* sweep.

MRS. LARUE. It was charming meeting all of you gentle-men, too.

130

HOWAY. Mr. Schellenbach, don't go! Joe, Stinker, don't go! Mother, let them stay here with us. Don't let them go. They're my mob.

> (MRS. LARUE *looks pained. She told* HOWAY *the mob cannot stay at Larue Towers. Why is he bringing it up again? But* EDDIE *is grinning at* HOWAY *as he gives him a playful chuck under the chin.*)

EDDIE. We couldn't do that, squirt. My mom wouldn't like it for me to move out. She'd come in here and clean out the place. You know my mom!

> (HOWAY *nods. Of course he knows Mrs. Schellenbach and he realizes that* EDDIE *has to get along with her. She is a determined character and he knows how determined mothers can be.*)

HOWAY. Yes, Mr. Schellenbach!

EDDIE. You come down to see us, squirt.

> (HOWAY *raises his eyes to his mother. Will she ever let him go down to Shantyland?*)

MRS. LARUE. Some day I will bring Howay down to see you, Mr. Schellenbach. (*Ah! She will come with him.*) I plan to give Ellsworth a gold piano. And after it has been delivered to him we will come in some afternoon between 3 and 3:30 and he can play for us.

EDDIE. (*He is uneasy.*) Well, Belle, I better put you wise to something. Ellsworth can't play on a real piano.

JOE. I will put you wise to something worse than that, Belle. He can't even play on a kitchen table—only on that shelf.

MRS. LARUE. No?

JOE. Yes.

MRS. LARUE. But I will send him a gold piano anyway

131

and maybe he can take lessons. Good night, gentle-men, I'll see you to the door.

EDDIE. We'd rather leave by the window. We feel more natural.

(*As he says this he makes for the window, followed by* JOE *and the* STINKER, *the silver clanking in their sacks. They wave—and then are gone.* HOWAY *sighs. Well, he has* MIMI *anyway. He has someone to play with.*)

HOWAY. Mother, what are you going to do about Mimi—? Mimi did everything.

MIMI. Oh yes, what about me? I did everything.

MRS. LARUE. Oh, of course she did—she is an adorable little darling. (*She takes* MIMI's *hand.*) And I was so rude to you.

MIMI. You were? When?

MRS. LARUE. She can have anything she wants—all the money, all the toys, all the pretty clothes. What do you want, dear?

HOWAY. Mother, since she got rid of the sticks, her own mother is mad at her. She can never never go back to the Blue, Blue Mountains again. She has no place to go.

MRS. LARUE. Mimi, is this true? (MIMI *nods her head.*) Oh, my dear child, how sad—how awful! What can I do for you, darling?

MIMI. I want to stay here with Howay.

HOWAY. She likes me, Mother. No matter how I treat her—she likes me.

MRS. LARUE. She has good taste, dear.

HOWAY. Why not, Mother? We have sixteen bathrooms and eighteen empty bedrooms——

132

MRS. LARUE. Don't you worry, Mimi. I will look after you. I will send you to the finest girl's school—out in La Jolla, California. I will call them tonight and you can ride on a big train tomorrow.

HOWAY. But Mother, she wants to stay here with us.

(*As* MRS. LARUE *has mentioned a girl's school,* MIMI *gets a look of alarm and runs over and stands close to* HOWAY.)

MRS. LARUE. I will always take care of her financially.

MIMI. I want to play with Howay.

MRS. LARUE. You'll have lots of little girls to play with out there, Mimi.

HOWAY. But gosh, Mother, she wants to stay here.

MRS. LARUE. Howay, that's enough. I know what I'm doing. Mimi, don't cry. You'll love it at Miss Fishcroft's. That's where I went to school when I was a little girl.

HOWAY. (*He turns away sulkily.*) Oh, darn it!

MRS. LARUE (*She walks to his side and speaks in a low tone.*) I can't keep her here, dear. I am afraid of her mother. Oh, Howay, if we had this child here, Mrs. McThing would be sure to come around. I couldn't face that. No—no—don't sulk, Howay. I mean no. Mimi—— (*She goes to* MIMI'S *side.*) It's a beautiful place out there. You'll have a pony to ride just like Howay's, a bicycle, swimming pool, dancing lessons; and they will be so kind to you. Let me show you a picture of the swimming pool out there. It's in the music room. (*She goes through the door to the right to get the picture of the swimming pool at Miss Fishcroft's.*)

(HOWAY *and* MIMI *are left alone on the stage. They*

133

look sad. MIMI *starts to run toward the window.*)

MIMI. Howay, come. Let's run away.

HOWAY. Gosh, I can't run away now. I have to stay here until I'm grown up, but then I'll go away and only come back for Christmas and my birthdays. I'm sorry, Mimi. I wish she'd let you stay.

MIMI. (*She has just thought of something. Hope springs into her eyes.*) Howay! I know. My mother—my mother will help me!

HOWAY. Your mother help you? She is off you for life. You disobeyed her when you chased the sticks. Your mother won't help you. You'll have to go to La Jolla.

MIMI. My mother *will* help me. (*She stands in the center of the room and stamps three times with her foot on the floor.*) MOTHER! MOTHER! MOTHER!

HOWAY. (*He grabs her arm.*) Mimi, don't do that! Don't do that!

(MRS. LARUE *comes back in the room. She walks to* MIMI *and pushes the pictures under her nose.*)

MRS. LARUE. Here is the swimming pool and here is a picture of Miss Fishcroft, the founder. She's been dead thirty years, but just look at that sweet face!

HOWAY. Mimi called her mother!

MRS. LARUE. Mimi called her mother! Mrs. McThing? (*She grows pale.*) Sybil! Nelson! (*She runs over and pulls the bell cord.*) Oh Mimi, why did you do that? She'll come. Oh Mimi, Mimi. How will I act? What shall I say? (*She has also thought, "How do I look?" and put her hand to her hair. She takes hold of the two children and takes them over to sit close beside her on the sofa. Her voice is clipped and dry as she*

134

talks to herself.) I'll be calm. What was that my father always said? Meet life gently and gently will it use you. I'll be gentle. That's how I'll be—gentle. But oh, how can I get gentle in a hurry?

>(SYBIL *and* NELSON *run down the stairs. What is happening now?*)

NELSON. Yes, ma'am. You rang.

MRS. LARUE. Sybil, Nelson, tell Jenkins at the gate not to let anyone in. Not anyone. I'm not at home to any-one—remember.

NELSON. (*They start up the stairs.*) Sure. (*To Sybil.*) Come on. Don't worry, Mrs. Larue, we'll see no one gets through that gate tonight. We've had enough company for one night. (*Then* SYBIL *lets out a shriek and* NELSON *backs away with a groan of terror.* NELSON *pushes* SYBIL *aside.*) Outta my way——

>(*He runs out the door through the music room and* SYBIL *runs after him, screaming,* "Ahhhhhhhhhhh-hhhh."
>
>*No wonder they screamed! At the top of the stairs there is a* WITCH! *She is wearing a high peaked hat. Her hair is long and matted and hangs like dirty dish-rags on either side of her long, thin wart-covered face. Her nose is long and sharp. Her arms are skinny and bony, flat as rulers. In one hand she is holding a long gnarled wooden stick.*
>
>*The lights have dimmed in the room. It seems as though she is so horrible that at the sight of her the lights wanted to go out, too. But she must have brought her own queer greenish light with her. She is standing in it. Perhaps it comes from*

135

her eyes, which roam the room like a cat's. She
begins to come slowly down the stairs.)

WITCH. (*Her voice is hoarse and croaking.*) Where—is—
my—child?

(*Now she is standing in the room, her bony hands
crossed over the stick.*

MRS. LARUE *is sitting with the children, her back
flattened against the sofa. She is stiff with terror.
HOWAY's eyes are popping and MIMI is cowering
down.*

MRS. LARUE *takes a big swallow and stands up. After
all, she must remember her manners no matter
how horrid this creature looks.*)

MRS. LARUE. (*Her teeth are chattering. Her voice is dry.
She speaks rapidly.*) Mrs. McThing, I believe! I must
say immediately that never again will I send a child
home. I'll let all of the little girls come in here and
play with my boy. And if they don't come—I will go
and look for them. I am not the same as I was. You
can watch me from your place in the Blue, Blue Mountains. You'll see that I have changed. Please give me
another chance.

WITCH (*not even looking at her*). Where is my child?

(MIMI *gets up off the sofa and walks slowly toward
the WITCH. HOWAY tries to pull her back. So does
MRS. LARUE.*)

HOWAY (*in low whisper*). Don't go, Mimi.

MRS. LARUE (*also in whisper*). Stay back, child.

(*But MIMI is going anyway. She looks frightened
but nevertheless she walks slowly but surely
across the room.*)

MIMI. H-huh—here I—am, Mo-mother!

WITCH (*turning the green cat's eyes upon her*). You! You betrayed your mother. You sided with humans. (MIMI *drops her head.*)

MRS. LARUE (*standing up in indignation*). But she's only a baby.

WITCH. (*Her eyes never leave* MIMI. MRS. LARUE *might be the wind.*) I picked you up off a dust heap when such as these threw you away.

MRS. LARUE. She only wanted someone to play with.

WITCH. I took you up to the Blue, Blue Mountains and showed you beauties never seen by them.

MRS. LARUE (*in a pleading tone*). Children never realize what we do for them.

WITCH. You listened and you told—

MRS. LARUE. Children always tell everything. They have no discretion.

WITCH. —so you could play with this boy!

MRS. LARUE. She was lonely with your bears and your chipmunks!

WITCH. Come back where you belong and I will hide you forever in here. (*Touches her heart.*) They will never see you again! Come—— (*She grabs* MIMI *by the arm and raises her stick to beat her as* MRS. LARUE *runs forward. Her eyes blazing, her cheeks red, she wrestles with the witch and seizes the stick from her.*)

MRS. LARUE. Take your hands off this child. You horrid old hag—— (*She beats her over the head.*) Hide her in your heart? You have no heart! Get out—get out! (*She beats the* WITCH *up the stairs and through the door.* MIMI *and* HOWAY *run to the bottom of the stair-*

137

way. In a second MRS. LARUE *comes back breathing rapidly. She still has the black stick.*) If you think I could let that horrid old hag have a lovely child—no, never. I—why I'm on the board of ten child protective associations. Never you mind, Mimi, you'll stay here with us and be our little daughter and our little sister.

HOWAY. (*He walks to his mother's side and speaks to her and looks at her as he has never done before.*) Mother, you're okay. I used to think you were two-thirds jerk, even if you were my mother. But you're all right. Boy, am I proud of you—shake? (*He extends his hand. They shake hands.*)

MRS. LARUE (*slowly*). Thank you, Howay. Thank you, son. You have never spoken to me like that before in all of your life. I don't believe I have ever been so happy. (*There is the sound of someone sobbing.*) What's that? (*She turns and sees* MIMI. *She has thrown herself on the steps. She is crying bitterly. They hurry to her.*) Don't cry, Mimi, don't be afraid. If she comes back I'll do it again. Whatever revenge she takes—we'll face it together, you and Howard and I.

MIMI (*standing up*). You beat her—you beat my mother!

MRS. LARUE. And she deserved it—that ugly creature.

MIMI (*throwing herself down on the stairs again*). She isn't ugly. She isn't—she isn't. She's beautiful and she didn't kiss me good-bye. Mother, oh Mother, Mother!
(*At this moment we hear again the tinkling "Be happy" music box music. It comes faintly at first and then louder and then we see at the top of the stairs, although we did not see how she came, a beautiful beautiful creature standing in a rosy light. This time many of the lights in the room*

138

have gone out, too. But now it is because they are discouraged. Who would look at them?

She has long golden hair, so long she has it wrapped over and over like a shawl on one arm.

*Her dress is silk, covered with little sparkling
things which glisten like stars when she moves
and her dress makes a whish-whooshing-swishing
sound. But it is not the kind of sound made by
anybody's silk dress. This sound is like the sound
made by a waterfall in a mountain canyon, or like
a forest of aspen trees when the wind blows
through them in October.*
This beautiful creature is raising MIMI *gently to her
feet.*)

MIMI (*joyfully*). Mother, Mother. I knew you'd come
back. You came to get me?

MOTHER. No. Only for this. (*She kisses her. She holds
her little face between her hands.*) My little girl!
You have left me forever? You have chosen them?

MIMI. I wanted to play with this boy.

MOTHER. I know. I know.

MIMI. Mother, will you ever come again?

MOTHER. No.

MIMI. Won't I ever see you or hear you or touch you
again?

MOTHER. No. But when you are happy—that will be I.

MIMI. Mother, my heart is breaking.

MOTHER. Yes. Yes.

MIMI. Is your heart breaking, too?

MOTHER (*drops her lovely head*). Yes. Yes.

MIMI. Let's press our broken hearts together and maybe
they will heal. (*They clasp each other closely.*)

140

MOTHER (*after a second*). Better now?

MIMI. Yes, is yours?

MOTHER. Yes, and now—— (*She turns and starts to move off.*)

MIMI. Don't say it, Mother. Don't say good-bye!

MOTHER. No, only good night. (*As she moves, she moves with a slight limp.*)

MIMI. Mother, Mother, you're limping. She hurt you, she did hurt you.

MOTHER. No, that's only my broken heart. (*She goes out of the door.* MIMI *watches her and now some of the lights come back on.*)

MIMI (*calling*). Wave to me, wave to me, Mother—at the window! (MIMI *now runs to the window and as she waves, raising her hand higher and higher we know that Mrs. McThing is flying higher and finally out of sight.* MIMI *stands looking out of the window. Her shoulders sag.*)

HOWAY. (*He goes to her.* MRS. LARUE *is behind him.*) Mimi, Mimi? (*She doesn't turn.*) Oh, Mimi—— (*This is the first time* HOWAY *has ever called her that she has not turned around quickly. He reaches out his hand and touches her.*) Mimi!

MIMI. (*She answers but does not turn.*) Yes.

HOWAY. Mimi, who was the ugly one—who was she?

MIMI (*not turning*). My mother.

HOWAY. You called the beautiful one mother, too. I don't understand.

MIMI. (*She turns now.*) Oh, sometimes when your mother is helping you—she has to *look* ugly.

(*And as she says this,* MIMI's *eyes are not really*

141

looking at HOWAY—*they are looking above his head and way, way off to the Blue, Blue Mountains and Mrs. McThing's white house in the tall trees which* MIMI *will never see again.*

But even in her imagination she will not stay there long because standing here waiting for her, is HOWAY!)

HOWAY. Mimi, let's play—let's play—— (*And then she is back. Here is Howay! She smiles.*)

MIMI. Oh yes, let's play—let's play—— (*She runs to him and* MRS. LARUE *smiles at them happily as the* CURTAIN *falls.*)